BELLWORK®

Reading/Language Arts

Level 5

BELLWORK®
Educational Materials

Author
Anne Gall

Contributing Author
Carrie Hernandez

Editorial Consultants:
Michelle N. Barnett
Kent A. De Pue
Erica Kaiser
Margaret Kinney

Illustrators:
José L. de la Rosa
Brenda Morales

The publisher wishes to thank the following educators who read portions of the series prior to publication for their comments and suggestions.

Rebecca Afghani
Linda Behrens
Pam Bluestein
Amy Brophy
Sue Buttera
Mary Johnson Cajiao
Mark Cohen
Marne Colby
Erika Daniels
Carey Davis

Ann DePierro
Victor Dorff
Don Felton
Kim Fortune
Robin Harbeck
Sheri Joseph
Rebecca Keene
Mia Lewis
Sarah Milam
Dennis Regus

Lauren Rips
Ona L. Sandi
Mindi Shapiro
Lynne Shisbey
Ruthie Smith
Kim Marra Stephenson
Kathy Terndrup
Alicia Trent
Jennifer Williams

BELLWORK
10529 Dale Avenue
PO Box 205
Stanton, CA 90680-0205

(800) 782-8869
Fax (714) 995-1181
www.bellwork.com

Printed in the U.S.A. (06/06)
ISBN 1-932469-25-7

Name _____

Fill in the bubble next to the words that correctly complete each *statement* or *question*.
Pay attention to the punctuation.

❶ _____ **your hair this morning?**

- Ⓐ You have combed
- Ⓑ Have you combed
- Ⓒ Comb, did you
- Ⓓ You combed

❷ _____ **here from Korea?**

- Ⓕ Did Kim come
- Ⓖ Kim will come
- Ⓗ Come, Kim will
- Ⓙ Kim came

❸ _____ **early tomorrow.**

- Ⓐ He should wake up
- Ⓑ Should he wake up
- Ⓒ Up should he wake
- Ⓓ Wake up should he

❹ Her socks _____ **in a few minutes.**

- Ⓕ get dry will
- Ⓖ dry will get
- Ⓗ will get dry
- Ⓙ will it dry

BELLWORK Reading/Language Arts • Level 5

Name _____

Fill in the bubble next to the answer that will form a complete sentence.

1

Ⓐ the big old grandfather clock
Ⓑ late in the afternoon
Ⓒ they saw many animals
Ⓓ today at school

2

Ⓕ yesterday at the library
Ⓖ since Mother left
Ⓗ in the winter
Ⓙ they waited and waited

3

Ⓐ after the bell rang
Ⓑ one chair was at the table
Ⓒ outside the cafeteria
Ⓓ Jason, one of my brothers

4

Ⓕ a very good story
Ⓖ because it rained
Ⓗ to walk the dog
Ⓙ the soldiers crossed the river

2

Name _____

1 Choose the word that tells exactly how the desk *looked*.

Ⓐ spicy
Ⓑ neat
Ⓒ soft
Ⓓ prompt

2 Choose the word that tells exactly how the pickle *tasted*.

Ⓕ green
Ⓖ creamy
Ⓗ sour
Ⓙ noisy

3 Choose the word that tells exactly how the CD *sounded*.

Ⓐ rough
Ⓑ loud
Ⓒ cool
Ⓓ shiny

4 Choose the word that tells exactly how the pillow *felt*.

Ⓕ white
Ⓖ quiet
Ⓗ sweet
Ⓙ fluffy

Name _____

Fill in the bubble next to the root (base) word for each <u>underlined word</u>.

❶ The root (base) of the word <u>worthless</u> is _____.

Ⓐ wor
Ⓑ less
Ⓒ wort
Ⓓ worth

❷ The root (base) of the word <u>disappear</u> is _____.

Ⓕ dis
Ⓖ pear
Ⓗ sap
Ⓙ appear

❸ The root (base) of the word <u>returning</u> is _____.

Ⓐ turn
Ⓑ re
Ⓒ ing
Ⓓ tune

❹ The root (base) of the word <u>reasonable</u> is _____.

Ⓕ son
Ⓖ reason
Ⓗ able
Ⓙ reasoning

4

Name _____

Choose the answer that *best* combines the numbered sentences into *one sentence*.

❶ Marta plays the piano. Marta plays the organ. Marta plays the guitar.

    Ⓐ Marta plays the piano and the organ and the guitar.

    Ⓑ Marta plays the piano, organ, and guitar.

    Ⓒ Marta plays the piano and organ, and she plays the guitar.

---

❷ The wind blew. It knocked down a tree. The wind blew so hard.

    Ⓕ The wind blew hard, knocked down a tree.

    Ⓖ A hard tree knocked down the wind.

    Ⓗ The wind blew so hard that it knocked down a tree.

Read the passage below. Then answer the questions on the next page. You may look back at this page as you answer the questions.

Have you been to a dude ranch? It sounds like fun! Many families enjoy this type of vacation.

Little kids can ride a small pony or a horse around in a ring with counselors teaching them and helping them to ride safely.

Ten- and eleven-year-olds learn about riding horseback. They have a horse assigned to <u>them</u> for a whole week. They can ride on trails with other kids their own ages.

Teenagers go camping and rafting; as well as, horseback riding in the mountains.

In the meantime, the parents can ride, or learn to ride, slow or fast, on trails or in the mountains. If they want to, they can go exploring on their own.

A big hearty breakfast is served every morning to give everyone energy for the day's activities. Everybody can go swimming and fishing. In the evenings, they have cookouts over a campfire, and there are sing-alongs and talent shows. People tell lots of stories about dude ranching experiences. Some people like to tell ghost stories too.

6

Name _____

1 **The term "dude ranching" means —**

Ⓐ living on a ranch.

Ⓑ riding horseback.

Ⓒ working on a ranch full-time.

Ⓓ staying on a ranch for a short time.

2 **In the third paragraph, the underlined word them refers to —**

Ⓕ little kids.

Ⓖ horses.

Ⓗ ten- and eleven-year-olds.

Ⓙ teenagers.

3 **After a full morning of dude ranching activities, what do you think will happen next?**

Ⓐ Everyone will go dancing.

Ⓑ Everyone will have time to rest.

Ⓒ The horses will canter around the ring.

Ⓓ The counselors will ride into the mountains.

4 **Mark F if the statement is a fact. Mark O if the statement is an opinion.**

_____ Dude ranching is fun.

_____ At a dude ranch, people may ride horses.

Name _____

Read each sentence and look at the <u>underlined words</u>. There may be a mistake in them. Select the best answer to correct the mistake. If there is no mistake, select *correct as is*.

---

❶ The minister <u>was very helping</u> to us.

Ⓐ was very helper
Ⓑ was very helpful
Ⓒ was very helped
Ⓓ correct as is

---

❷ The new <u>sofa was not comforts</u>.

Ⓕ sofa was not comfort
Ⓖ sofa was not comforted
Ⓗ sofa was not comfortable
Ⓙ correct as is

---

❸ The <u>bodybuilder was muscle</u>.

Ⓐ bodybuilder was mass
Ⓑ bodybuilder was muscles
Ⓒ bodybuilder was muscular
Ⓓ correct as is

---

❹ The two countries <u>made an agreement</u>.

Ⓕ made an agreeing
Ⓖ made an agreeable
Ⓗ made an agreed
Ⓙ correct as is

8

Name _____

Choose the *best* topic sentence (main idea) for each paragraph.

❶ _____ Teal blue, a dull blue-green, is seen on the wings of a bird called the "blue-winged teal." Another shade of blue, aquamarine, gets its name from the color of seawater. Indigo was once made from a plant and is a deep violet blue. Navy, a very dark blue, is used for the U.S. Navy uniforms.

Ⓐ Aquamarine is watery.

Ⓑ Indigo is made from a plant and is a deep violet blue.

Ⓒ There are many shades of blue.

Ⓓ Indigo is a plant.

❷ _____ They live in Australia. The mother kangaroo has a pouch on the front of her body in which to carry her baby. Males grow as large and as heavy as men. However, kangaroos can hop over objects six feet high and go as fast as forty miles per hour.

Ⓕ Kangaroos can hop very fast.

Ⓖ Male kangaroos grow very large.

Ⓗ Kangaroos are very unusual animals.

Ⓙ A mother "roo" carries her baby in a pouch.

9

Name _____

Mark the mistakes in the following letter. Put ≡ under letters that should be capitals. Put ∧ to show where punctuation marks have been omitted. Can you find twenty (20) mistakes?

1

250 vermont avenue

los angeles California 90004

february 5 2005

dear hannah

Please come to my slumber party on valentine's day try to come in time for

dinner at six oclock Dont forget to bring your pajamas

yours truly

Amani

Name _____

Fill in the bubble next to the words that correctly complete each *statement* or *question*.
Pay attention to the punctuation.

1 _____ **my pencil on your desk?**

- Ⓐ That is
- Ⓑ Is that
- Ⓒ Those are
- Ⓓ Where

2 _____ **they live.**

- Ⓕ That is where
- Ⓖ Is that where
- Ⓗ Where is that
- Ⓙ What is

3 _____ **coming home?**

- Ⓐ Where you are
- Ⓑ When are you
- Ⓒ Who are you
- Ⓓ When you

4 _____ **come home tomorrow.**

- Ⓕ Will my mom
- Ⓖ Mom, will you
- Ⓗ Who will
- Ⓙ My mom will

BELLWORK Reading/Language Arts • Level 5

Name _____

Read this composition and answer the question that follows.

My hero is my father. My father is a fireman. My father works at the fire station in Anaheim, California. My father fought the fire at Laguna, too. The fire at Laguna was very hard to fight. Laguna has many hills and canyons and it had a lot of dry brush. My father helped to save many homes.

1 **What suggestion would you make to the student who wrote this?**

Ⓐ Put in your father's name.

Ⓑ Tell where Laguna is.

Ⓒ Combine some of the sentences.

Ⓓ Tell why your father is your hero.

Name _____

Read each set of sentences and decide if one of the underlined words is spelled *incorrectly*, or if there is *no mistake*. Choose your answer and fill in the bubble.

1

Ⓐ Cody changed the tire when it went flat.

Ⓑ We are going to the movie tonite.

Ⓒ The dog ran around the block.

Ⓓ no mistake

2

Ⓕ Noah finished the project early.

Ⓖ She tripped over her shoelaces.

Ⓗ Tell me why you don't like me.

Ⓙ no mistake

3

Ⓐ Tabitha chaced the crow away.

Ⓑ That knife is very sharp.

Ⓒ The movie was really weird.

Ⓓ no mistake

4

Ⓕ I know which college I am going to attend.

Ⓖ The cattle are safe in the field.

Ⓗ Throuw the ball to Amanda.

Ⓙ no mistake

13

Read the passage below. Then answer the questions on the next page. You may look back at this page as you answer the questions.

Whistling can be fun. Have you learned to whistle? For some people it seems to be easy. Others have a hard time learning to hold their lips just right while moving air in or out.

Some people say whistling makes <u>them</u> feel happy. They whistle a tune that they remember, or they whistle along with music from a radio, tape, or CD.

It's fun to try to imitate birds. From your library, you may be able to check out recordings of birdcalls. You can spend many <u>delightful</u> hours listening to the special sounds made by each species of bird and trying to make the same sounds they do.

You don't have to pay a lot of money for an instrument or take lessons in order to have fun and make music. You can just whistle.

Name _____

1 The underlined word <u>them</u> refers to —

Ⓐ a whistle.

Ⓑ some people.

Ⓒ whistling.

Ⓓ birds.

2 <u>Delightful</u> means —

Ⓕ light.

Ⓖ from the light.

Ⓗ full of delight.

Ⓙ deli ful.

3 At the library you may —

Ⓐ whistle.

Ⓑ pay for an instrument.

Ⓒ find recordings.

Ⓓ imitate birds.

4 Write the letter <u>F</u> if the statement is a fact.

Write the letter <u>O</u> if the statement is an opinion.

___ Whistling is easy for everyone.

___ Whistling makes everybody feel happy.

Name _____

For each item below, choose the word that means *the same or almost the same* (synonym) as the <u>underlined word</u>.

1 <u>folks</u> means —

Ⓐ famous
Ⓑ full
Ⓒ fall
Ⓓ people

2 a <u>wild</u> horse is —

Ⓕ animal
Ⓖ tame
Ⓗ untamed
Ⓙ will

3 <u>labor</u> means —

Ⓐ while
Ⓑ work
Ⓒ weary
Ⓓ idle

4 <u>absent</u> means —

Ⓕ present
Ⓖ advise
Ⓗ away
Ⓙ remainder

Name _____

Read each sentence. Choose the word(s) that show the meaning of the <u>underlined contraction</u>.

1 **Alonzo <u>hadn't</u> won a game all day long.**

Ⓐ had ent

Ⓑ had net

Ⓒ had not

Ⓓ has not

2 **I think <u>she'll</u> show up sometime soon.**

Ⓕ she will

Ⓖ she heel

Ⓗ shell will

Ⓙ she well

3 **She <u>won't</u> be in the play.**

Ⓐ won not

Ⓑ will not

Ⓒ was not

Ⓓ won nut

4 **He <u>can't</u> find his lunchbox.**

Ⓕ can nut

Ⓖ ca not

Ⓗ can to

Ⓙ cannot

BELLWORK Reading/Language Arts • Level 5

Name _____

Read each sentence and look at the <u>underlined words</u>. There may be a mistake in them. Select the best answer to correct the mistake. If there is no mistake, select *correct as is*.

1 The dog <u>barked louded</u>.

   Ⓐ barked louding

   Ⓑ barked loud

   Ⓒ barked loudly

   Ⓓ correct as is

2 <u>She floated lazily</u> in the pool.

   Ⓕ She floated lazy

   Ⓖ She floated laze

   Ⓗ She floated lazier

   Ⓙ correct as is

3 He drove the car <u>too faster</u>.

   Ⓐ too fast

   Ⓑ too fastly

   Ⓒ too fasten

   Ⓓ correct as is

4 She <u>bowled very best</u>.

   Ⓕ bowled very good

   Ⓖ bowled very well

   Ⓗ bowled very better

   Ⓙ correct as is

Name _____

Fill in the bubble next to the word that correctly completes each sentence.

1 They _____ good friends.

   Ⓐ are   Ⓑ is

2 Both of them _____ broccoli.

   Ⓕ eats   Ⓖ eat

3 Mr. Lee _____ my troop leader.

   Ⓐ was   Ⓑ were

4 He _____ nice clothes.

   Ⓕ have   Ⓖ has

5 It _____ getting close to Passover.

   Ⓐ is   Ⓑ are

6 Gina _____ a lot of milk.

   Ⓕ drink   Ⓖ drinks

7 My dog _____ chasing my cat.

   Ⓐ was   Ⓑ were

8 They _____ in-line skates.

   Ⓕ have   Ⓖ has

Read the passage below. Then answer the questions on the next page. You may look back at this page as you answer the questions.

Do you watch the news on TV? What do you do when you see something scary? Something horrible? Something "yucky"? Do you ignore it? Change the channel? Discuss it with brothers, sisters, or parents? Do you bring up those happenings when your class discusses current events? Do you ask someone to try to explain it to you?

If you see something you don't understand, or if something you see upsets you, don't let it "bug" you. Ask somebody for an explanation. Find a book, magazine, or newspaper article on the subject. Find its location on a world map. Ask your librarian in the reference section to suggest sources of information.

Learning doesn't come only from textbooks. The things we learn by asking questions are often very meaningful to us. Finding out about the things you see on TV news programs may make them much less frightening.

Name _____

1 **This passage is mainly about —**

Ⓐ finding out more about movies.

Ⓑ finding out more about newspapers.

Ⓒ finding out more about libraries.

Ⓓ finding out more about the news on TV.

2 **The *main idea* of this passage is how you could —**

Ⓕ watch the news.

Ⓖ learn in school.

Ⓗ react to the news.

Ⓙ find a map.

3 **It is important to find out about disturbing events because —**

Ⓐ we can ignore them.

Ⓑ we can go to the library.

Ⓒ we can better understand them.

Ⓓ we can change the channel.

4 **Put a Y in front of the things you could do or an N in front of the things that you should not do if you see pictures on TV of a cat caught in floodwaters.**

____ Find the location of the flood.

____ Ask someone why there is a flood.

____ Find out who is supposed to rescue cats.

____ Try to rescue the cat yourself.

21

Name _____

Choose the sentence (detail) that *best* supports the topic sentence (main idea) for the paragraph.

❶ **Jane's cat was named Tiger. _____**
Tiger liked to sleep on Jane's bed. There he purred and purred.

Ⓐ Tiger was Jane's cat.

Ⓑ Tiger purred and purred.

Ⓒ He got his name because he was striped.

❷ **Television programs can be educational. _____**
There are programs for learning how to cook, sew, or fix a house. There are classes to help little kids learn how to sound out words. Other channels offer college classes.

Ⓕ I like to read a good book.

Ⓖ Dad wants a big screen TV.

Ⓗ Some programs help us learn how to do new things.

Name _____

In each group, fill in the bubble next to the word that comes *first* in alphabetical order.

❶
- Ⓐ nail
- Ⓑ might
- Ⓒ list
- Ⓓ kite

❷
- Ⓕ silver
- Ⓖ sand
- Ⓗ same
- Ⓙ seat

❸
- Ⓐ while
- Ⓑ weather
- Ⓒ without
- Ⓓ word

❹
- Ⓕ energy
- Ⓖ exciting
- Ⓗ every
- Ⓙ enough

23

Name _____

Fill in the bubble next to the answer that correctly completes each sentence.

1 We _____ a good movie last night.

  Ⓐ see

  Ⓑ saw

  Ⓒ seen

  Ⓓ seed

2 Do you know what she _____?

  Ⓕ do

  Ⓖ done

  Ⓗ did

  Ⓙ doing

3 The package hasn't _____ yet.

  Ⓐ came

  Ⓑ comed

  Ⓒ come

  Ⓓ coming

4 We are _____ to use computers.

  Ⓕ learn

  Ⓖ learned

  Ⓗ learning

  Ⓙ learnt

Name _____

Use the table of contents to answer each question. Fill in the bubble next to the *best* answer.

Table of Contents

	Page
Writing 1
Nature 10
Hawaii 17
Old Woman 25
Today and Tomorrow 33

1 In which part of the book would this table of contents appear?

Ⓐ on the cover
Ⓑ front part
Ⓒ title page
Ⓓ back part

2 The chapter most likely to contain information about volcanoes begins on page _____.

Ⓕ 1
Ⓖ 17
Ⓗ 33
Ⓙ 25

3 You might begin reading about birds and butterflies on page _____.

Ⓐ 1
Ⓑ 25
Ⓒ 10
Ⓓ 33

4 The chapter most likely to contain a poem about the future begins on page _____.

Ⓕ 10
Ⓖ 25
Ⓗ 17
Ⓙ 33

25

Name _____

Read each set of sentences and decide if one of the <u>underlined words</u> is spelled *incorrectly*, or if there is *no mistake*. Choose your answer and fill in the bubble.

❶

Ⓐ Alberto made a great <u>catch</u>.

Ⓑ Sarah was <u>cent</u> to a new classroom.

Ⓒ I am tired of <u>waiting</u> for them.

Ⓓ no mistake

❷

Ⓕ The fossils that we saw were very well <u>preserved</u>.

Ⓖ In the <u>storm</u>, a fierce wind blew.

Ⓗ Jonathan made an <u>errer</u> on his math test.

Ⓙ no mistake

❸

Ⓐ How can we <u>train</u> our bird to talk?

Ⓑ One good <u>deed</u> deserves another.

Ⓒ The lion's <u>maine</u> is thick and yellow.

Ⓓ no mistake

❹

Ⓕ The pine trees are <u>straeght</u> and tall.

Ⓖ The <u>traffic</u> was terrible today.

Ⓗ My last name is hard for people to <u>pronounce</u>.

Ⓙ no mistake

Name _____

Fill in the bubble next to the answer that is punctuated correctly.

1 **When are you** _____

Ⓐ going

Ⓑ going?

Ⓒ going.

Ⓓ going,

2 **How is Madison** _____

Ⓕ feeling.

Ⓖ feeling

Ⓗ feeling!

Ⓙ feeling?

3 **I'll go with** _____

Ⓐ you?

Ⓑ you

Ⓒ you.

Ⓓ you,

4 **My Uncle José won a lot of** _____

Ⓕ money,

Ⓖ money!

Ⓗ money?

Ⓙ money

Read the passage below. Then answer the questions on the next page. You may look back at this page as you answer the questions.

Does your class do choral reading? Do you sing in a chorus? If so, you're all reading or singing the same piece at the same time. Some of your voices are high, and others are pitched lower. Perhaps someone reads or sings a part alone. It happens that way in a symphony, too. A symphony orchestra is a group of people playing music together. It's sort of like your class doing a choral reading or singing in a chorus.

However, a symphony orchestra is not divided according to which instruments can play high or low notes. A symphony orchestra is divided into sections according to how the instruments are played and the sounds they make. The sections are strings, woodwinds, brass, and percussion.

Stringed instruments are played by pulling a bow (containing many strings) across a few tuned strings or by plucking the strings with your fingers. Woodwinds and brass are played by blowing air into them or across an opening. Most <u>percussion</u> instruments are played by hitting them, either with your hand or using sticks of different kinds.

Although the musicians are playing the same piece of music, different instruments are playing different notes, some high, some low. Like a chorus, the instruments combine to make beautiful sounds we call music.

Name _____

1 How many sections are in a symphony orchestra?

Ⓐ one

Ⓑ two

Ⓒ three

Ⓓ four

2 Percussion instruments are played —

Ⓕ with a bow.

Ⓖ by blowing.

Ⓗ by hitting.

Ⓙ by singing.

3 Fill in the bubble in front of the sentence that is <u>true</u>.

Ⓐ All musical instruments sound the same.

Ⓑ All musical instruments are played the same.

Ⓒ Stringed instruments are played by blowing on them.

Ⓓ none of the above

4 You can tell that the author —

Ⓕ plays the horn.

Ⓖ does choral reading.

Ⓗ sings in a chorus.

Ⓙ thinks orchestral music is beautiful.

29

Name _____

Fill in the bubble next to the sentence that explains the figure of speech (idiom).

1 **Gus thought the test was <u>a piece of cake</u>. He was sure that he passed it.**

Ⓐ The test was hard.

Ⓑ The test took a long time.

Ⓒ The test was easy.

Ⓓ The test tasted good.

2 **Peggy won the drawing contest and was <u>on cloud nine</u>.**

Ⓕ Peggy was very happy.

Ⓖ Peggy thought it might rain.

Ⓗ Peggy was sad.

Ⓙ Peggy rode on a cloud.

3 **The doctor declared that Claudia was <u>fit as a fiddle</u> and didn't need to return to the hospital.**

Ⓐ Claudia can play the fiddle.

Ⓑ Claudia is healthy.

Ⓒ Claudia is a nurse.

Ⓓ Claudia is sick.

4 **After eating the spoiled food, Ryan was <u>as sick as a dog</u>. He stayed in bed for three days.**

Ⓕ Ryan was a dog.

Ⓖ Ryan was sick a little bit.

Ⓗ Ryan ate dog food.

Ⓙ Ryan was very sick.

Name _____

Use the example below from a thesaurus to answer the questions that follow.

John used his thesaurus to find a synonym for <u>beautiful</u>.

> **beautiful** adj. adorable, charming, comely, cute, elegant, gorgeous, lovely. *See*: attractive (*Ant.*) homely, plain, ugly.

Read this sentence.

I gave my wife, Shay, <u>beautiful</u> flowers for her birthday.

❶ **Which of the following words would be the *best* choice for John to use to replace <u>beautiful</u> in the sentence?**

Ⓐ ant.

Ⓑ homely

Ⓒ gorgeous

Ⓓ plain

❷ **What other word might John look up in the thesaurus to find a synonym for <u>beautiful</u>?**

Ⓕ ugly

Ⓖ cute

Ⓗ attractive

Ⓙ homely

❸ **Which word could John use as an antonym for <u>beautiful</u>?**

Ⓐ ant.

Ⓑ homely

Ⓒ cute

Ⓓ charming

Name _____

Fill in the bubble next to the word (antonym) that correctly completes each sentence.

❶ The *opposite* of <u>sharp</u> is —

Ⓐ smart.
Ⓑ dull.
Ⓒ beautiful.
Ⓓ pointed.

❷ The *opposite* of <u>cooked</u> is —

Ⓕ raw.
Ⓖ boiled.
Ⓗ baked.
Ⓙ ripe.

❸ The *opposite* of <u>fresh</u> is —

Ⓐ new.
Ⓑ young.
Ⓒ fried.
Ⓓ stale.

❹ The *opposite* of <u>friend</u> is —

Ⓕ hate.
Ⓖ pal.
Ⓗ enemy.
Ⓙ chum.

Name _____

Using the dictionary entry below, choose the *best* answer to each question.

---

al•pha•bet (al´ · fə · bet) n. the letters that form the elements of written language. [< Greek *alpha* a + *beta* b]

---

❶ To alphabetize is to put words in —

Ⓐ an invitation.

Ⓑ ABC order.

Ⓒ an elementary school.

---

❷ The first letter of the <u>Greek</u> alphabet is —

Ⓕ a.

Ⓖ alpha.

Ⓗ beta.

❸ The second letter of the <u>Greek</u> alphabet is —

Ⓐ alpha.

Ⓑ beta.

Ⓒ kappa.

❹ Number the following words in alphabetical order.

___ language

___ elements

___ form

___ letters

33

Name _____

1 The prefix "un–" means "not."
Knowing this helps you to know that
<u>un</u>even means —

Ⓐ not even.

Ⓑ very even.

Ⓒ equal.

Ⓓ none of the above

2 The prefix "re–" means "again."
Knowing this helps you to know that
<u>re</u>write means —

Ⓕ to write the first time.

Ⓖ to write something over and over.

Ⓗ to write something again.

Ⓙ to not write.

3 The prefix "pre–" means "before."
Knowing this helps you to know that
<u>pre</u>school happens —

Ⓐ during school.

Ⓑ after school.

Ⓒ with school.

Ⓓ before school.

4 The prefix "dis–" means "not."
Knowing this helps you to know that
<u>dis</u>own means —

Ⓕ to own later.

Ⓖ to not own.

Ⓗ to own again.

Ⓙ to never own.

34

Name _____

Fill in the bubble next to the word that correctly completes each sentence.

1 The _____ have gone fishing.

Ⓐ boyes
Ⓑ boyies
Ⓒ boys
Ⓓ bois

2 There is snow on both _____.

Ⓕ mountain
Ⓖ mountainous
Ⓗ mountains
Ⓙ mountaines

3 We had two _____ last month.

Ⓐ party
Ⓑ parties
Ⓒ partys
Ⓓ partyes

4 They divided the apple into two _____.

Ⓕ half
Ⓖ halfs
Ⓗ halfes
Ⓙ halves

Name _____

Fill in the bubble next to the correct answer.

1 **In the word hate<u>ful</u>, the "–ful" makes the word mean —**

Ⓐ having no hate.

Ⓑ full of hate.

Ⓒ less hate.

Ⓓ lots of hats.

2 **In the word quiet<u>ly</u>, the "–ly" makes the word mean —**

Ⓕ in a quiet way.

Ⓖ without quiet.

Ⓗ to sleep.

Ⓙ one who is quiet.

3 **In the word paint<u>er</u>, the "–er" makes the word mean —**

Ⓐ having color.

Ⓑ mixing paint.

Ⓒ a picture.

Ⓓ one who paints.

4 **In the word wire<u>less</u>, the "–less" makes the word mean —**

Ⓕ to send a telegram.

Ⓖ having wires.

Ⓗ without wires.

Ⓙ installing electricity.

Name _____

Use the dictionary entry to answer the questions below.

> **crest** (krest) n.   **1.** a bunch of feathers on the head of a bird.   **2.** top of a hill.   **3.** the ridge of a wave.

❶ **Which of the above meanings fits the sentence below?**

The cardinal has a bright red <u>crest</u>.

Ⓐ Definition **1**   Ⓑ Definition **2**   Ⓒ Definition **3**

❷ **Which of the above meanings fits the sentence below?**

The surfer took off on the <u>crest</u> of the sea.

Ⓕ Definition **1**   Ⓖ Definition **2**   Ⓗ Definition **3**

❸ **Which of the above meanings fits the sentence below?**

The hikers climbed to the mountain <u>crest</u>.

Ⓐ Definition **1**   Ⓑ Definition **2**   Ⓒ Definition **3**

BELLWORK Reading/Language Arts • Level 5

Read the passage below. Then answer the questions on the next page. You may look back at this page as you answer the questions.

Have you decided what kind of job you want when you grow up? Do you like working inside or would you rather be outdoors?

Emily, a city girl, thought about what she would like to do when she grew up. Emily liked school and teachers and thought about being a teacher. She took piano lessons and sang well but didn't have enough talent to be successful in show business. At one time Emily thought she wanted to help sick people. However, a visit to a hospital changed her mind about that.

On Career Day, Emily's mother invited her daughter to the data processing office. She got to use one of the computers for a little while. However, Emily didn't like the idea of being "tied to a desk" for hours like her mother was. She missed being able to go outdoors. Emily and her mother didn't even leave the building for lunch!

Then this city girl remembered camp and how much she had enjoyed being outside in the fresh air. Emily decided that, when she grew up, she would look for an outdoor job.

Name _____

1 **This passage is mainly about —**

(A) living in the city.

(B) Emily's choices of careers.

(C) taking music lessons.

(D) using a computer.

2 **Being "<u>tied to a desk</u>" means —**

(F) she had strings tied around her legs.

(G) she couldn't leave home.

(H) she sat in one place for hours.

(J) she has a job outdoors.

3 **The passage says Emily liked —**

(A) being outdoors.

(B) hospitals.

(C) inside work.

(D) an office.

4 **Write the name of at least one career at which Emily could work outdoors.**

_____

_____

_____

39

Name _____

Fill in the bubble next to the sentence that is punctuated correctly.

1
- Ⓐ Lian yelled "Alex, don' touch my toys!"
- Ⓑ Lian yelled, Alex, don, touch my toys!"
- Ⓒ Lian yelled, "Alex, don't touch my toys!"
- Ⓓ Lian yelled, "Alex, don't touch my toys!

2
- Ⓕ The class read the poem, "The Log Cabin," by Irene Reardon.
- Ⓖ The class read the poem "The Log Cabin by Irene Reardon.
- Ⓗ The class read the poem, The Log Cabin" by Irene Reardon.
- Ⓙ The class read the poem The Log Cabin by Irene Reardon.

3
- Ⓐ Katie's favorite song is "The Dance."
- Ⓑ Katie's favorite song is The Dance."
- Ⓒ Katie's favorite song is "The Dance.
- Ⓓ Katie's favorite song is The Dance.

4
- Ⓕ Today, I read the short story, A Train."
- Ⓖ Today, I read the short story, "A Train."
- Ⓗ Today, I read the short story, "A Train.
- Ⓙ Today, I read the short story, A Train.

Name _____

Read this composition. Then answer the question that follows.

They chose a president, a vice president, a secretary, and a treasurer. They decided what kind of books the members should read and how often the club should meet. Two of them wanted to be first to tell about books they read. Names were written on a piece of paper and put into a basket. Then the president picked out one name.

1 **What suggestion would you make to the student who wrote this?**

Ⓐ Tell who the members are.

Ⓑ At the beginning, put in a sentence that states the topic.

Ⓒ Tell why they need a treasurer.

Ⓓ Tell how often they will meet.

Name _____

Mark the part of each sentence that needs a capital letter. If no capital is needed, mark
"none."

1 The movie was shot   in new York.   none
   Ⓐ   Ⓑ   Ⓒ   Ⓓ

2 They called   him   "mr. Funnyman."   none
   Ⓕ   Ⓖ   Ⓗ   Ⓙ

3 Lake superior is one of the Great Lakes.   none
   Ⓐ   Ⓑ   Ⓒ   Ⓓ

4 The White House is on   Pennsylvania Avenue.   none
   Ⓕ   Ⓖ   Ⓗ   Ⓙ

Name _____

Choose the word (homophone) that will complete each sentence correctly.

1 **Did your glasses _____?**

Ⓐ break   Ⓑ brake

2 **A _____ of geese flew by.**

Ⓕ pair   Ⓖ pear

3 **Sean _____ like to go to college.**

Ⓐ would   Ⓑ wood

4 **That happened long ago in the _____.**

Ⓕ past   Ⓖ passed

5 **The _____ needs to be repaired.**

Ⓐ rode   Ⓑ road

6 **Janet got some new _____ for her birthday.**

Ⓕ close   Ⓖ clothes

Name _____

Using the encyclopedia pictured below, fill in the bubble next to the correct answer.

1 In which volume would you learn about Scotland?

Ⓐ 10

Ⓒ 11

Ⓑ 12

Ⓓ 13

2 In which volume would you find out how many legs an insect has?

Ⓕ 1

Ⓗ 6

Ⓖ 7

Ⓙ 12

3 In which volume would you learn about a lady named Rosa Parks?

Ⓐ 3

Ⓒ 9

Ⓑ 10

Ⓓ 11

4 In which volume would you learn about the purchase of Alaska?

Ⓕ 1

Ⓗ 4

Ⓖ 8

Ⓙ 10

Name _____

Read each group of words. Then choose the word that does *not* belong.

1   leopard   tiger   elephant   forest
      Ⓐ   Ⓑ   Ⓒ   Ⓓ

2   Venus   Jupiter   telescope   Earth
      Ⓕ   Ⓖ   Ⓗ   Ⓙ

3   baseball   football   checkers   tennis
      Ⓐ   Ⓑ   Ⓒ   Ⓓ

4   pictures   mysteries   adventures   fables
      Ⓕ   Ⓖ   Ⓗ   Ⓙ

5   shark   tuna   sailboat   dolphin
      Ⓐ   Ⓑ   Ⓒ   Ⓓ

6   bicycle   skateboard   in-line skates   sled
      Ⓕ   Ⓖ   Ⓗ   Ⓙ

45

Name _____

Read each set of sentences and decide if one of the underlined words is spelled *incorrectly*, or if there is *no mistake*. Choose your answer and fill in the bubble.

1
- Ⓐ She found ten <u>scents</u> in her pocket.
- Ⓑ How much <u>information</u> does he need from me?
- Ⓒ We went to a wonderful <u>concert</u>.
- Ⓓ no mistake

2
- Ⓕ The ducks were <u>waiding</u> in the pond.
- Ⓖ Marianne's birthday is in <u>August</u>.
- Ⓗ How many <u>tickets</u> do I need?
- Ⓙ no mistake

3
- Ⓐ Kelly <u>received</u> an award today.
- Ⓑ We need a new <u>mowse</u> for our computer.
- Ⓒ <u>Autumn</u> is the season between summer and winter.
- Ⓓ no mistake

4
- Ⓕ The bird costs <u>twise</u> as much as the fish.
- Ⓖ My sister <u>hid</u> in a tree at the park.
- Ⓗ A dog can be <u>loyal</u> and true to its owner.
- Ⓙ no mistake

Name _____

Use the dictionary entry to answer the questions below.

box (boks) n. **1.** small section of seats in a theater or sports arena. **2.** a carton to hold things. v. **3.** to put things in a box. **4.** to fight another in a boxing match.

Which of the above meanings fits each sentence below?

---

1 **I need a large square <u>box</u>.**
- Ⓐ Definition 1
- Ⓑ Definition 2
- Ⓒ Definition 3
- Ⓓ Definition 4

2 **Before moving, we <u>boxed</u> up a lot of things.**
- Ⓕ Definition 1
- Ⓖ Definition 2
- Ⓗ Definition 3
- Ⓙ Definition 4

3 **The <u>box</u> seat was more expensive.**
- Ⓐ Definition 1
- Ⓑ Definition 2
- Ⓒ Definition 3
- Ⓓ Definition 4

4 **My dad likes to watch fighters <u>box</u>.**
- Ⓕ Definition 1
- Ⓖ Definition 2
- Ⓗ Definition 3
- Ⓙ Definition 4

Name _____

1 Which of the following is <u>not</u> a form of poetry?

   Ⓐ haiku

   Ⓑ cinquain

   Ⓒ diamanté

   Ⓓ fiction

2 A haiku poem uses a specific format of 5, 7, 5. These numbers stand for what?

   Ⓕ number of lines

   Ⓖ number of words

   Ⓗ number of syllables

   Ⓙ number of letters

3 An example of a nonfiction story might be —

   Ⓐ <u>The Talking Cat</u>.

   Ⓑ <u>The Hungry Boy</u>.

   Ⓒ <u>The Flying Elephant</u>.

   Ⓓ <u>The Walking Fish</u>.

4 An example of a fictional story might be —

   Ⓕ <u>George Washington, Our First President</u>.

   Ⓖ <u>Native Americans of the West</u>.

   Ⓗ <u>Reptiles</u>.

   Ⓙ <u>My Fairy Godmother</u>.

Name _____

Fill in the bubble next to the sentence that explains the figure of speech (idiom).

1 **In London, it was raining cats and dogs. The streets and sidewalks were flooded.**

Ⓐ It was raining a lot.

Ⓑ It was raining only in London.

Ⓒ It wasn't raining at all.

Ⓓ The rain was making the animals upset.

2 **On the first day of school I had butterflies in my stomach. I held my mom's hand until I saw some of my friends.**

Ⓕ I ate something bad.

Ⓖ I was tired from playing.

Ⓗ I saw some beautiful butterflies.

Ⓙ I was nervous.

3 **Dana said that I am the spitting image of my older sister. We both have the same color hair. We are both tall and have lots of freckles.**

Ⓐ My older sister and I don't look alike.

Ⓑ I look like my cousin, more than my sister.

Ⓒ I look like my sister.

Ⓓ My older sister spit on me once.

4 **My dance teacher told us to break a leg at the dance recital. We practiced all year and now was our big chance.**

Ⓕ She really wanted us to get hurt.

Ⓖ She wanted us to fall down.

Ⓗ She wanted us to do our best.

Ⓙ She wanted us to make fools of ourselves.

49

Read the passage below. Then answer the questions on the next page. You may look back at this page as you answer the questions.

In some schools, baseball seems to be the favorite team sport. In others, the students like basketball better. How are these games different and how are they alike?

Baseball requires a large area, usually outdoors, such as a playground or park. At home kids can practice hitting and catching baseballs or softballs in yards, alleys, or fields. Basketball can be played either outdoors on dirt or blacktop or indoors on a wooden floor. Many boys and girls practice shooting balls through a hoop fastened onto their home or garage.

As you know, a baseball team needs nine members, a bat and a small ball. Basketball teams are composed of five members and use a larger ball. Both baseball and basketball have leagues so kids can play after-school games.

There are many ways to <u>participate</u> in these sports, such as one-on-one or "monkey move-up," donkey baseball or wheelchair basketball. If you don't play on a team, maybe you can be a scorekeeper, a referee, an umpire, or just enjoy cheering for your favorite team.

Name _____

1 **In which way are basketball and baseball alike?**

Ⓐ team sports

Ⓑ use a bat

Ⓒ usually played indoors

2 **In which way are basketball and baseball different?**

Ⓕ can be practiced at home

Ⓖ have leagues

Ⓗ number of members on a team

3 **The word <u>participate</u> means to —**

Ⓐ have no part of.

Ⓑ take part in.

Ⓒ leave.

4 **On the lines below, write at least six compound words found in this passage.**

_____

_____

_____

_____

51

Look at the timeline below. Then answer the questions on the following page. You may look back at this page as you answer the questions.

| Apollo 7 is the first manned mission to orbit the Earth for the United States. | Apollo 8 is the first manned spacecraft to orbit the Moon for the United States. | Apollo 13 is launched but suffers an explosion. The crew returns safely. | Apollo 14 is launched. The legendary Alan Shepard becomes the first man to hit a golf ball on the Moon. | Apollo 15 astronauts drive the first moon rover. | The American Apollo 18 and the Soviet Soyuz 19 have the first international spacecraft rendezvous. |

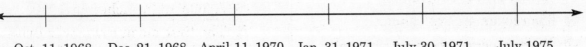

Oct. 11, 1968   Dec. 21, 1968   April 11, 1970   Jan. 31, 1971   July 30, 1971   July 1975

Name _____

1 **This timeline helps the reader to**
_____.

Ⓐ find out about space exploration throughout history

Ⓑ learn about some of the U.S. Apollo missions

Ⓒ locate events in astronauts' lives

Ⓓ know what other countries were exploring space

2 **What happened during the Apollo 13 mission?**

Ⓕ It landed on the Moon.

Ⓖ It orbited the Moon.

Ⓗ There was an explosion.

Ⓙ Thirteen crew members hit golf balls on the moon.

3 **How many years passed between the launching of Apollo 15 and Apollo 18?**

Ⓐ 3 years

Ⓑ 4 years

Ⓒ 5 years

Ⓓ 6 years

4 **Which of these is an opinion from this timeline?**

Ⓕ Apollo 8 was the best space mission.

Ⓖ Apollo 13 launched in 1970.

Ⓗ The first moon rover was driven on the Apollo 15 mission.

Ⓙ Apollo 18 and Soyuz 19 had a joint mission.

Name _____

Fill in the bubble in front of the sentence that is worded correctly.

1

Ⓐ It was a nice concert.

Ⓑ It was a nicely concert.

Ⓒ It was a nicest concert.

3

Ⓐ She sang so beautiful.

Ⓑ She sang so beautifully.

Ⓒ She sang more beautiful.

2

Ⓕ I would go again glad.

Ⓖ I would go again glader.

Ⓗ I would go again gladly.

4

Ⓕ He is stronger than John.

Ⓖ He is strongest than John.

Ⓗ He is more stronger than John.

Name _____

Mark the part of each sentence that needs a capital letter. If no capital is needed, mark "none."

1 Presidents' day   honors   Washington and Lincoln.   none
    (A)   (B)   (C)   (D)

2 Her name   was   mrs. Cabbage.   none
    (F)   (G)   (H)   (J)

3 The teacher   read   *Amanda the great*.   none
    (A)   (B)   (C)   (D)

4 Baltimore   is in   the state of maryland.   none
    (F)   (G)   (H)   (J)

55

Name _____

Fill in the bubble next to the letter or letters needed to spell the incomplete word in each sentence. Then write the complete word on the dotted line.

1 How many c___ns do you have in your pocket?

Ⓐ ou

Ⓑ oa   _ _ _ _ _ _ _ _ _ _ _ _ _ _

Ⓒ oe

Ⓓ oi

2 I'm sorry you misunderst___d what I said.

Ⓕ oo

Ⓖ ew   _ _ _ _ _ _ _ _ _ _ _ _ _ _

Ⓗ ue

Ⓙ oe

3 Haley said, "I am my mother's d___ghter."

Ⓐ oo

Ⓑ aw   _ _ _ _ _ _ _ _ _ _ _ _ _ _

Ⓒ au

Ⓓ a

4 There's no water coming out of the f___ntain.

Ⓕ oo

Ⓖ ow   _ _ _ _ _ _ _ _ _ _ _ _ _ _

Ⓗ oi

Ⓙ ou

Name _____

Fill in the bubble next to the correct word (pronoun).

1 **Joseph yelled at _____.**

- Ⓐ me
- Ⓑ I
- Ⓒ he
- Ⓓ she

2 **Mother made lunch for _____.**

- Ⓕ he
- Ⓖ I
- Ⓗ we
- Ⓙ us

3 **Libby handed the book to _____.**

- Ⓐ hers
- Ⓑ she
- Ⓒ her
- Ⓓ they

4 **_____ thought the game was fun.**

- Ⓕ Me
- Ⓖ Him
- Ⓗ He
- Ⓙ His

Name _____

Read each sentence. Fill in the bubble next to the words that make a <u>prepositional phrase</u>.

1 **Timmy was playing in the tree house.**

- Ⓐ Timmy was
- Ⓑ Timmy was playing
- Ⓒ playing in the tree house
- Ⓓ in the tree house

2 **Under the bridge, there were three billy goats.**

- Ⓕ Under the bridge
- Ⓖ Under the bridge, there were
- Ⓗ there were three billy goats
- Ⓙ three billy goats

3 **The ball hit me on my head.**

- Ⓐ The ball
- Ⓑ The ball hit me
- Ⓒ hit me on my head
- Ⓓ on my head

4 **The spider was spinning a web above the windowsill.**

- Ⓕ The spider was spinning
- Ⓖ The spider was spinning a web
- Ⓗ spinning a web
- Ⓙ above the windowsill

58

Name _____

Read each sentence. Fill in the bubble next to the two words that were blended to mak the underlined word.

1 On Mother's Day we all went to **brunch** at my mom's favorite restaurant.

Ⓐ brunch and crunch

Ⓑ breakfast and lunch

Ⓒ break and munch

Ⓓ lunch and dinner

2 My brother was working on the **Internet** to research his report.

Ⓕ internal and net

Ⓖ interesting and nets

Ⓗ international and network

Ⓙ network and intern

3 With so many cars and trucks drivin on our streets, you can see the **smog** in most big cities.

Ⓐ smoke and fog

Ⓑ smile and frog

Ⓒ smoke and dog

Ⓓ hog and smart

4 On our vacation, my family stayed in a **motel**.

Ⓕ mom and telephone

Ⓖ telephone and motor

Ⓗ hotel and motel

Ⓙ motor and hotel

Read the passage below. Then answer the questions on the next page. You may look back at this page as you answer the questions.

Smoking is a nasty and dangerous habit. Smokers leave the burned-out ends of their cigarettes in ashtrays which become black with soot and tar. Smoking causes rooms and clothing to become smelly and walls to be coated with a yellow stain. Careless smokers sometimes toss their cigarettes along the streets and highways and cause fires. At other times, when the smoker goes to sleep, a lit cigarette, cigar, or pipe could drop and <u>ignite</u> the furniture or curtains close by. People have died in fires like that.

Almost a third of all cancer deaths are due to smoking. There are many things in tobacco smoke that can cause cancer or tumors in smokers and in nonsmokers who breathe other people's smoke. Two of those chemicals, nicotine and carbon monoxide, are poisonous. Tobacco causes the blood vessels and breathing passages to become narrowed and coated with tar. That can block the flow of blood and oxygen to the brain, heart, and lungs. Many men and women die of lung cancer as a result of smoking.

Don't let your friends talk you into smoking. Once you start, it may be almost impossible for you to stop. (Nicotine is addictive to many smokers.) If you must be around someone who is smoking, try to go outside or to another room away from the poisonous fumes.

Name _____

1 **Fill in the bubble next to the sentence that is an *opinion*.**

Ⓐ Cigarettes, cigars, and pipes use tobacco.

Ⓑ Lungs need clear breathing passages.

Ⓒ Smoking is nasty.

Ⓓ Cigarettes can cause fires.

2 **The word <u>ignite</u> means —**

Ⓕ not very smart.

Ⓖ to pay no attention.

Ⓗ stain.

Ⓙ to set on fire.

3 **From this passage, you can tell that the author —**

Ⓐ smokes.

Ⓑ thinks that smoking is impossible.

Ⓒ thinks that smoking is an unhealthy habit.

Ⓓ is careless.

4 **Write <u>F</u> if the statement is a fact. Write <u>O</u> if the statement is an opinion.**

____ Smoking is one cause of lung cancer.

____ Some ingredients in tobacco smoke are poisonous.

____ The easiest way to quit smoking is to just stop.

61

Name _____

Choose the answer that *best* completes each sentence.

① **He liked ham and cheese, but** _____ _____.

- Ⓐ he liked roast beef
- Ⓑ he ate them anyway
- Ⓒ he hated green vegetables
- Ⓓ he made a sandwich

② **If it rains tomorrow,** _____ _____.

- Ⓕ we had snow
- Ⓖ it will be dry and hot
- Ⓗ we'll go another time
- Ⓙ the sun will shine all day

③ **Stay here until** _____ _____.

- Ⓐ your mother picks you up
- Ⓑ the bus didn't come
- Ⓒ you can't go on the trip
- Ⓓ your brother left

④ **Jon went to the dentist because** _____.

- Ⓕ his tooth hurt
- Ⓖ his father went fishing
- Ⓗ the dentist's office was closed
- Ⓙ it was dark

62

Name _____

Choose the answer that will form a complete sentence.

❶ _____ **are going on a field trip.**

    Ⓐ The fifth grade students
    Ⓑ Where
    Ⓒ To the zoo
    Ⓓ Next week

❷ _____ **are very fragrant.**

    Ⓕ In the garden
    Ⓖ When they open
    Ⓗ Blooming
    Ⓙ The flowers blooming in my yard

❸ _____ **wrote some other good stories.**

    Ⓐ On the computer
    Ⓑ The author
    Ⓒ In school
    Ⓓ Because she liked to

❹ _____ **is red, white, and blue.**

    Ⓕ In July
    Ⓖ Flying in the wind
    Ⓗ The flag of the United States
    Ⓙ Now

63

Name _____

Fill in the bubble next to the word that will complete <u>both</u> sentences.

1 Our class went to see a _____ in the auditorium.
We like to _____ soccer.

Ⓐ drama
Ⓑ movie
Ⓒ play
Ⓓ watch

2 They dug a _____ in the backyard.
He felt _____ this morning.

Ⓕ healthy
Ⓖ hole
Ⓗ tired
Ⓙ well

3 Nicole _____ the new baby, Anthony.
Yesterday, I _____ my mother at her job.

Ⓐ talked
Ⓑ called
Ⓒ phoned
Ⓓ named

4 The painting is a _____ of art.
The teacher said I need to _____ on my math skills.

Ⓕ work
Ⓖ toil
Ⓗ job
Ⓙ product

64

Name _____

Using the dictionary entry below, choose the *best* answer to each question.

---

u•ni•corn (yōo´ · nə · kôrn) n.   a fabulous horselike animal.
[< L *uni-* one + *cornu* a horn]

---

❶ A <u>unicorn</u> is —

Ⓐ a horse.

Ⓑ a two-horned animal.

Ⓒ a one-horned animal.

❷ A <u>unicycle</u> has —

Ⓕ one wheel.

Ⓖ two wheels.

Ⓗ three wheels.

❸ A <u>cornet</u> is —

Ⓐ a grain of corn.

Ⓑ an angle.

Ⓒ a musical instrument which is blown into.

❹ People who wear a <u>uniform</u> —

Ⓕ wear different kinds of clothing.

Ⓖ wear the same kind of clothing.

Ⓗ form a committee.

Name _____

Mark the mistakes in the following dialogue. Put ≡ under letters that should be capitals.
Put ^ to show where punctuation marks have been omitted. Circle any misspellings.
Can you find twelve (12) mistakes?

Come here to me, she said.   when are you going to clean your room

Bob answered,   will saturday be soon enuf

Name _____

Choose the sentence that is the *best* topic sentence (main idea) for each paragraph.

1 _____ **We'll have our usual math and language classes and a special assembly before lunch. This afternoon we will have our school pictures taken.**

Ⓐ When the bell rings, we'll go to recess.

Ⓑ We are in fifth grade at Roosevelt School.

Ⓒ We're going to have a busy day at school.

2 _____ **Gold and silver are used for rings, necklaces, bracelets, pins, and hair ornaments. Gems, such as pearls, rubies, and opals make jewelry even more beautiful.**

Ⓕ Gold and silver are used for rings and bracelets.

Ⓖ Most jewelry is made with gold, silver, and gems.

Ⓗ Gems are beautiful.

BELLWORK Reading/Language Arts • Level 5

Name _____

Choose the *best* answer to each question below.

1 To make a turkey sandwich, first you get the bread and then you cut the bread in half and put it on the plate. What is missing?

Ⓐ You need to put everything away.

Ⓑ You need to get out a bowl.

Ⓒ You need to put the turkey on the bread.

2 Which order is correct to get ready for school?

Ⓕ Put on your clothes, take a shower, get your backpack.

Ⓖ Take a shower, put on your clothes, get your backpack.

Ⓗ Get your backpack, put on your clothes, take a shower.

3 In order to ride a bike, you must first put on your helmet. Then you sit on the seat, and finally you need to do what?

Ⓐ Press on the brakes.

Ⓑ Tell your friend where you are going.

Ⓒ Push the pedals.

4 To brush your teeth, you take the brush and scrub your teeth, then you rinse. What is missing?

Ⓕ You need to put toothpaste on the brush.

Ⓖ You need to gargle.

Ⓗ You need to fill the sink with water.

Name _____

Read each sentence. Fill in the bubble next to the word(s) that is the <u>appositive</u>.

❶ Mrs. Barnett, my first grade teacher, has red hair.

Ⓐ Mrs. Barnett
Ⓑ my first grade teacher
Ⓒ has red hair

❷ Some of my friends, including the ones from school, are coming to my party.

Ⓕ Some of my friends
Ⓖ including the ones from school
Ⓗ are coming to my party

❸ A number of Presidents, including Roosevelt and Kennedy, have died in office.

Ⓐ A number of Presidents
Ⓑ including Roosevelt and Kennedy
Ⓒ have died in office

❹ Billy, my next door neighbor, is going to the game with us.

Ⓕ Billy
Ⓖ my next door neighbor
Ⓗ is going to the game with us

Read the passage below. Then answer the questions on the next page. You may look back at this page as you answer the questions.

When you read the word <u>record</u>, what do you think it means? Do you think of a famous <u>Book of World Records</u>? Maybe you think about the process involved when an artist <u>records</u> music or a storyteller <u>records</u> a story on a disc or tape. Have you heard music played on an old-fashioned <u>record</u> player? Have you done an experiment at school in which you had to <u>record</u> the growth rate of a plant or the daily temperature?

How will you know which meaning of <u>record</u> the author intended?

Read the entire sentence in which you find the word <u>record</u>. If you don't understand it, reread the sentence or the entire paragraph. More than likely, some other words in that sentence or paragraph will give you a clue as to the word's meaning. Figuring out whether <u>record</u> is used as a noun or as a verb will give you another clue.

Name _____

Fill in the bubble next to the correct answer for question 1. Then fill in the bubble in front of the correct meaning of the word <u>record</u> in questions 2, 3, and 4.

---

1 He set a speed <u>record</u>. In this sentence, the word <u>record</u> is a —

Ⓐ verb.

Ⓑ noun.

Ⓒ pronoun.

---

2 The band went to the studio to <u>record</u> their latest song. <u>Record</u> means —

Ⓕ put music onto a disc or tape.

Ⓖ a CD or tape.

Ⓗ the latest song.

Ⓙ notes on the music.

---

3 He broke the <u>record</u> for the 50-yard dash. <u>Record</u> means —

Ⓐ music tape.

Ⓑ took notes.

Ⓒ made a disc.

Ⓓ fastest time.

---

4 The secretary made a <u>record</u> of the actions taken at the meeting. <u>Record</u> means —

Ⓕ played a song.

Ⓖ the best yet done.

Ⓗ read a story.

Ⓙ written report.

BELLWORK Reading/Language Arts • Level 5

Name _____

Using the encyclopedia pictured below, fill in the bubble next to the correct answer.

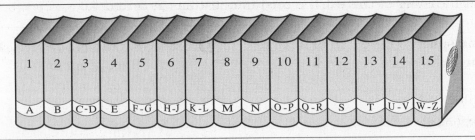

1 In which volume could you find out about South Africa?

ⒶＡ 2   Ⓒ 4

Ⓑ 7   Ⓓ 12

2 In which volume would you find a map of the United States?

Ⓕ 7   Ⓗ 8

Ⓖ 14   Ⓙ 15

3 In which volume could you find out more about Hans Christian Andersen?

Ⓐ 1   Ⓒ 3

Ⓑ 6   Ⓓ 9

4 In which <u>two</u> volumes would you look to find out which birds live in Peru?

Ⓕ 2 and 10   Ⓗ 2 and 5

Ⓖ 2 and 14   Ⓙ 2 and 7

Name _____

Read each sentence and look at the <u>underlined words</u>. There may be a mistake in them.
Select the best answer to correct the mistake. If there is no mistake, select *correct as is*.

---

1 **Give me some more of <u>them beans</u>, please.**

Ⓐ this beans

Ⓑ that beans

Ⓒ those beans

Ⓓ correct as is

---

2 <u>**This one is**</u> **mine.**

Ⓕ These one is

Ⓖ This here one is

Ⓗ The one is

Ⓘ correct as is

---

3 <u>**These skateboard**</u> **belongs to Ethan.**

Ⓐ This skateboard

Ⓑ That there skateboard

Ⓒ This here skateboard

Ⓓ correct as is

---

4 **Jasmine likes <u>this cheese sandwiches</u>.**

Ⓕ them there cheese sandwiches

Ⓖ these here cheese sandwiches

Ⓗ these cheese sandwiches

Ⓘ correct as is

73

Name _____

Fill in the bubble next to the word that is punctuated correctly.

1 **She wanted to read _____ book.**

Ⓐ Marks

Ⓑ Marks'

Ⓒ Mark's

Ⓓ Marks?

2 **What's for _____**

Ⓕ lunch?

Ⓖ lunch.

Ⓗ lunch,

Ⓙ lunch'

3 **Chloe liked the _____ in the art book.**

Ⓐ pictures

Ⓑ pictures"

Ⓒ picture's

Ⓓ pictures'

4 **We took our dog to ____ Johnson.**

Ⓕ Dr

Ⓖ Dr,

Ⓗ Dr'

Ⓙ Dr.

Name _____

Fill in the bubble next to the letter or letters needed to spell the incomplete word in each sentence. Then write the complete word on the dotted line.

---

1 ___ster comes in the springtime.

Ⓐ Ee

Ⓑ Ei   _ _ _ _ _ _ _ _ _ _ _ _ _

Ⓒ Eu

Ⓓ Ea

---

2 That program doesn't ___terest me.

Ⓕ un

Ⓖ in   _ _ _ _ _ _ _ _ _ _ _ _ _

Ⓗ ien

Ⓙ en

---

3 Sheila was ___bedient to ___er mother.

Ⓐ a

Ⓑ u   _ _ _ _ _ _ _ _ _ _ _ _ _

Ⓒ o

Ⓓ oa

---

4 You need a c___mma in that sentence.

Ⓕ a

Ⓖ oa   _ _ _ _ _ _ _ _ _ _ _ _ _

Ⓗ ow

Ⓙ o

BELLWORK Reading/Language Arts • Level 5

Read the passage below. Then answer the questions on the next page. You may look back at this page as you answer the questions.

In the early days in America, the colonists needed iron for farming tools, horseshoes, and parts for horse-drawn carts, wagons, and carriages. They also needed nails, candle holders, cooking pots, and barrel hoops. The iron barrel hoops were used in making barrels for shipping tobacco and cotton back to England.

It took a long time to get supplies from England by boat. The colonists could grow much of what they needed. They grew vegetables and fruits, and raised animals for food. They grew cotton and cut wool from their sheep for cloth. Builders used the native trees and clay for houses. However, products made of iron had to be ordered from Europe.

Some of the colonists knew how to make iron from the iron ore they found. They built blast furnaces in Virginia in 1621 and in Massachusetts in 1634. (In fact, George Washington's father ran an <u>ironworks</u> in about 1739.)

In a blast furnace, charcoal was added to the iron ore to make the fire hot enough to turn the ore into liquid. Then it was poured into molds or "*pigs*." With this and other processes, the colonists could make the things they needed.

Name _____

1 **Supplies for the colonies came from England —**

Ⓐ quickly.

Ⓑ slowly.

Ⓒ to Washington.

Ⓓ by air.

2 **Blast furnaces —**

Ⓕ melt iron ore.

Ⓖ heat homes.

Ⓗ mine iron ore.

Ⓙ make horseshoes.

3 **The early colonists needed iron for —**

Ⓐ factories.

Ⓑ trains.

Ⓒ tools.

Ⓓ cloth.

4 **The compound word <u>ironworks</u> means —**

Ⓕ a factory that makes iron.

Ⓖ the work of ironing.

Ⓗ work in a building made of iron.

Ⓙ tools for curling hair.

77

Name _____

Below is a partial list of endnotes from the back of a book. Look at the endnotes, then answer the following questions.

[1] Rivard, Laura. *Animal Extinction*. Chicago: Kaiser Publishing, p. 204.

[2] Herron, Jay Randall. "The Reason Why." *Our Animals*. July 2004, pp. 35–38.

[3] Kancho, Ara. *Saving Our Animals*. San Francisco: Barnett Books, pp. 105–127.

[4] Unter, David. "Everlasting Animals." *Animal Poems*. Seattle: Loo Publications, 2003, p. 14.

1 "The Reasons Why" is probably _____.

Ⓐ a book
Ⓑ a poem
Ⓒ an author
Ⓓ an article

2 What pages were referenced in *Saving Our Animals*?

Ⓕ p. 204
Ⓖ pp. 35–38
Ⓗ pp. 105–127
Ⓙ p. 14

Name _____

Fill in the bubble to show whether the <u>underlined word(s)</u> are the complete subject or the complete predicate in each sentence.

1 <u>Her favorite book</u> is *Southern Tales*.

   Ⓐ complete subject
   Ⓑ complete predicate

2 <u>It</u> was written by Ann Chadney.

   Ⓕ complete subject
   Ⓖ complete predicate

3 This book of folktales <u>contains stories from rural North Carolina and Virginia</u>.

   Ⓐ complete subject
   Ⓑ complete predicate

4 <u>Ms. Chadney</u> heard these old folktales and wrote them down.

   Ⓕ complete subject
   Ⓖ complete predicate

79

Name _____

Using this map of Beach Park, fill in the bubble next to the correct answer.

1 How many cars can be parked at this area of Beach Park?

Ⓐ 3　　　Ⓑ 4　　　Ⓒ 10　　　Ⓓ 12

2 To go from your car to the water, you must go _____.

Ⓕ north　Ⓖ south　Ⓗ east　Ⓙ west

3 How many fire rings are south of the lifeguard stand?

Ⓐ 1　　　Ⓑ 2　　　Ⓒ 3

4 To go from the picnic table to the lifeguard stand, you must go _____.

Ⓕ north　Ⓖ south　Ⓗ east　Ⓙ west

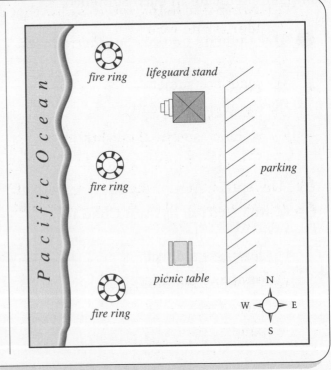

Pacific Ocean

fire ring

lifeguard stand

parking

fire ring

picnic table

fire ring

N
W ◆ E
S

8

Name _____

1 The suffix "–er" means "one who ___."
Knowing this helps you to know that a
build**er** is one who —

Ⓐ destroys things.

Ⓑ builds things.

Ⓒ ruins things.

Ⓓ watches shows about buildings.

2 The suffix "–able" means "capable of."
Knowing this helps you to know that
treat**able** means —

Ⓕ treated in the past.

Ⓖ many treatments.

Ⓗ more treatments.

Ⓙ can be treated.

3 The suffix "–ness" means "the state of
being." Knowing this helps you to
know that happ**iness** means —

Ⓐ not happy.

Ⓑ more happy.

Ⓒ being happy.

Ⓓ satisfied.

4 The suffix "–ful" means "full of."
Knowing this helps you to know that
joy**ful** means —

Ⓕ full of joy.

Ⓖ less joy.

Ⓗ more joy.

Ⓙ no joy.

Name _____

Using the dictionary's *guide words*, fill in the bubble next to the word that would be defined on that page.

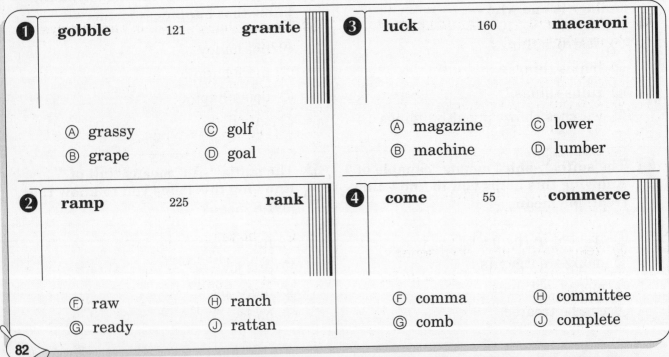

1   **gobble**   121   **granite**

   Ⓐ grassy   Ⓒ golf

   Ⓑ grape   Ⓓ goal

3   **luck**   160   **macaroni**

   Ⓐ magazine   Ⓒ lower

   Ⓑ machine   Ⓓ lumber

2   **ramp**   225   **rank**

   Ⓕ raw   Ⓗ ranch

   Ⓖ ready   Ⓙ rattan

4   **come**   55   **commerce**

   Ⓕ comma   Ⓗ committee

   Ⓖ comb   Ⓙ complete

Name _____

Read each sentence and look at the <u>underlined words</u>. There may be a mistake in them. Select the best answer to correct the mistake. If there is no mistake, select *correct as is*.

❶ That carpenter <u>can builds a good house</u> for you.

- Ⓐ can built a good house
- Ⓑ can build a good house
- Ⓒ can building a good house
- Ⓓ correct as is

❷ <u>Yesterday, Aunt Robyn sent</u> away for some flower bulbs.

- Ⓕ Yesterday, Aunt Robyn send
- Ⓖ Yesterday, Aunt Robyn sending
- Ⓗ Yesterday, Aunt Robyn sends
- Ⓙ correct as is

❸ <u>Bowser has aten</u> all of the kitten's food!

- Ⓐ Bowser has eat
- Ⓑ Bowser has ate
- Ⓒ Bowser has eaten
- Ⓓ correct as is

❹ <u>Who took my</u> quarter?

- Ⓕ Who taken my
- Ⓖ Who taked my
- Ⓗ Who tooking my
- Ⓙ correct as is

83

Read the passage below. Then answer the questions on the next page. You may look back at this page as you answer the questions.

Black-eyed Susan stood straight and tall. Her petals reflected the rays of the yellow sun as it moved across the sky. Her brown eyes were even darker than the soil in which she had been planted.

She was jealous as she watched puffs of milkweed floating past. Susan wished that she, too, could travel in the air. She tried and tried to pull free of her roots and fly away. She was even jealous of the leaves that fluttered briefly in the air before dropping to earth. Oh, how Susan wanted to fly!

One morning she heard Katie and her friend, Alyssa, talking in the garden. "Guess what," Katie said to Alyssa. "I'm going to go visit Grandma! I'm going to fly in a plane!"

Hearing that, Black-eyed Susan's head drooped. She thought, "Katie gets to fly, but Alyssa and I will be staying right here."

Early on the day they were to leave, Katie and her mother came into the garden. Katie asked, "Can we take some of these flowers to Grandma?" Her mother replied, "I think that's a lovely idea." Oh, how surprised and happy Susan was then!

Name _____

① The *main idea* of this passage is —

Ⓐ Susan had brown eyes.

Ⓑ Susan was straight and tall.

Ⓒ Susan wanted to fly.

Ⓓ Katie is going to visit Grandma.

② Black-eyed Susan was —

Ⓕ a girl.

Ⓖ a flower.

Ⓗ a grandma.

Ⓙ a mother.

③ Number the following sentences in the order in which they happened.

___ Katie told Alyssa about going to see Grandma.

___ Susan heard the girls talking in the garden.

___ Susan's head drooped.

___ Susan watched the sun go across the sky.

④ Write a sentence telling what you think happened next.

_____

_____

_____

_____

Name _____

Fill in the bubble next to the *best* source of information.

1 **To find the comic section, look in —**

ⒶⒶ an encyclopedia.

Ⓑ a glossary.

Ⓒ an atlas.

Ⓓ a newspaper.

3 **In your textbook, where would you find the meaning of the word <u>gracious</u>?**

Ⓐ the table of contents

Ⓑ the index

Ⓒ the glossary

Ⓓ a library

2 **Where would you look for a book about rain forests?**

Ⓕ an almanac

Ⓖ a library

Ⓗ a book of records

Ⓙ a dictionary

4 **To find out how to pronounce the word <u>photosynthesis</u>, look in —**

Ⓕ an atlas.

Ⓖ a newspaper.

Ⓗ an index.

Ⓙ a dictionary.

Name _____

Fill in the bubble in front of the answer that will *best* form *one complete sentence*.

1 **The house next door** _____.

Ⓐ is white with green trim
Ⓑ is white. Has green trim
Ⓒ is white, it has green trim
Ⓓ is white it has green trim

2 **The wise, old owl** _____.

Ⓕ hooted in the forest, he scared away the mouse
Ⓖ hooted in the forest whether he scared away the mouse
Ⓗ hooted in the forest. The mouse was scared
Ⓙ hooted in the forest and scared away the mouse

3 **She fell** _____.

Ⓐ and cut her hand and she bruised her hand
Ⓑ and cut and bruised her hand
Ⓒ and cut her hand and she also bruised her hand
Ⓓ and cut her hand, she bruised it too

4 **I got up, went** _____.

Ⓕ and then we studied science
Ⓖ to school at school studied science
Ⓗ studied science
Ⓙ to school, and then studied science

87

Name _____

Fill in the bubble next to the answer that correctly completes each sentence.

1 Yesterday, he _____ to the principal's office.

Ⓐ report
Ⓑ reports
Ⓒ reporting
Ⓓ reported

2 The men are _____ for deer.

Ⓕ hunt
Ⓖ hunted
Ⓗ hunting
Ⓙ hunts

3 Lupe hopes the deer will _____.

Ⓐ escape
Ⓑ escaping
Ⓒ escaped
Ⓓ escapes

4 I'll be glad when my baby sister _____ to walk.

Ⓕ learn
Ⓖ learned
Ⓗ learning
Ⓙ learns

88

Name _____

Choose the correct answer.

1 **Choose the word that shows Cori was *happy*.**

Ⓐ sat
Ⓑ frowned
Ⓒ scowled
Ⓓ smiled

2 **Choose the word that shows Brett was *helpful*.**

Ⓕ toot
Ⓖ aided
Ⓗ knew
Ⓙ often

3 **Choose the word(s) that show Hadil was *upset*.**

Ⓐ sang
Ⓑ cried
Ⓒ blew bubbles
Ⓓ grinned

4 **Choose the words that show people *respected* Alric.**

Ⓕ paid attention to him
Ⓖ walked away from him
Ⓗ laughed at him
Ⓙ ordered him

89

Read the passage below. Then answer the questions on the next page. You may look back at this page as you answer the questions.

You've probably read that George Washington was Commander-in-Chief in the Revolutionary War and our first President, but not so much has been written about his boyhood.

He was born in 1732 on a farm in the British colony known as Virginia. When he was three years old, the family moved to a much larger farm up the Potomac River. His only playmates were his brothers and sisters.

When George was about seven, the family moved again, and he started going to school. He studied arithmetic, geography, and history. George copied rules of behavior and memorized them. He was a good listener and treated everyone with respect. His love of math helped George in his first job as a surveyor.

When George was only eleven, his father died. As he grew older, he helped manage the farm, learning about planting and harvesting and the need to keep good records. Life was hard, but he learned to be patient, to stay calm under pressure, and continue with a job until it was done. By the time his schooling was over, George could keep complete and accurate accounts for the farm and write excellent business and friendly letters.

George Washington showed patience and understanding of other people's feelings and ideas. These traits, developed in childhood, and his knowledge of history, helped Washington become an outstanding leader in the formation of our country.

Name _____

1 From this passage you can tell that —

Ⓐ George was the youngest child in his family.

Ⓑ Virginia would become a state.

Ⓒ most young men go to college.

Ⓓ none of the above

---

2 This passage is part of a —

Ⓕ drama.

Ⓖ novel.

Ⓗ biography.

Ⓙ fable.

3 From this passage you can *conclude* that —

Ⓐ George Washington liked to farm.

Ⓑ George Washington's father was sick.

Ⓒ George Washington's childhood training was important.

Ⓓ George Washington went to college.

---

4 Number the following in the order in which they happened.

___ His father died.

___ George went to school.

___ The family moved to a bigger farm.

___ George Washington became a leader of our country.

Name _____

Read each set of sentences and decide if one of the <u>underlined words</u> is spelled *incorrectly*, or if there is *no mistake*. Choose your answer and fill in the bubble.

 1

Ⓐ We're going to Yosemite for our <u>vacation</u>.

Ⓑ My favorite fruit is a <u>pair</u>.

Ⓒ How long until we get to our <u>destination</u>?

Ⓓ no mistake

 2

Ⓕ <u>Together</u>, we make a great team.

Ⓖ My <u>neighbor</u> played football in college.

Ⓗ Leah is <u>always</u> late to everything.

Ⓙ no mistake

 3

Ⓐ The doctor <u>examined</u> my arm.

Ⓑ Robert is absent because he has an upset <u>stomache</u>.

Ⓒ Carmen is the <u>cutest</u> girl in my class.

Ⓓ no mistake

 4

Ⓕ We are sorry about losing the glove you <u>lent</u> us.

Ⓖ I know the <u>anser</u> to that question.

Ⓗ The <u>amusement</u> park was really crowded on Saturday.

Ⓙ no mistake

Name _____

Number each group of words in alphabetical order.

1

____ heart
____ hurt
____ hoof
____ hide

2

____ thing
____ those
____ threw
____ theme

3

____ child
____ cane
____ circle
____ cease

4

____ Theodore Roosevelt
____ John Hancock
____ Franklin Roosevelt
____ Benjamin Franklin

Name _____

Use this list of Latin or Greek roots and their meanings to answer the questions.

Root	Meaning		Root	Meaning
cred	believe		*bio*	life
cyc	circle		*vis*	see

1 The fireworks were _____. I could not believe how pretty they were.

Which word correctly completes the sentence?

Ⓐ cycle   Ⓒ incredible

Ⓑ visor   Ⓓ biopsy

2 My younger brother has a tricycle and I have a _____. My bike has only one wheel.

Which word correctly completes the sentence?

Ⓕ unicycle   Ⓗ credit

Ⓖ visionary   Ⓙ biography

3 The runway was not _____ through the storm. The pilot couldn't see where to land the plane.

Which word correctly completes the sentence?

Ⓐ recycle   Ⓒ bionics

Ⓑ credenza   Ⓓ visible

4 Kim took a _____ class and studied the different life forms of animals and plants.

Which word correctly completes the sentence?

Ⓕ biology   Ⓗ credential

Ⓖ creed   Ⓙ visit

Name _____

Choose the correct answer.

1 **A biography is a story about what?**

Ⓐ yourself

Ⓑ an animal

Ⓒ a person

Ⓓ a place

2 **Joseph read a book about the migration of whales. This is an example of what kind of literature?**

Ⓕ a fairy tale

Ⓖ a drama

Ⓗ a nonfictional story

Ⓙ a fictional tale

3 **Abby wrote a story about herself. She told where she was born, where she grew up, and other interesting facts about herself. This is an example of what kind of story?**

Ⓐ a biography   Ⓒ a fairy tale

Ⓑ an autobiography   Ⓓ a comic

4 **Our librarian told us to choose a book from the nonfiction section. Which of these books might be found there?**

Ⓕ The Day I Turned Into a Frog

Ⓖ Firefighters

Ⓗ My Teacher is a Mouse

Ⓙ World's Funniest Jokes

Name _____

Choose the sentence (detail) that *best* supports the topic sentence (main idea) for each paragraph.

❶ **The invention of the fountain pen made writing with ink much easier for students. Before its invention, a bottle of ink sat in a hole in the top of each student's desk. The student had to dip the point of a pen into the bottle of ink frequently. The pen points were scratchy and spattered ink.** _____

Ⓐ A fountain pen, however, held its own supply of ink.

Ⓑ Students are in fifth grade.

Ⓒ Felt pens come in many colors.

❷ **Mongeese were brought to Hawaii to get rid of rats, but that plan didn't work. Mongeese sleep at night when the rats come out to look for food.** _____

Ⓕ The mongoose looks something like a big squirrel.

Ⓖ Now Hawaii has lots of mongeese.

Ⓗ Hawaii was made a state in 1959.

Name _____

Choose the answer that *best* combines the numbered sentences into *one sentence*.

1 **Fruits are good for us. It is good for us to eat green vegetables. Yellow vegetables are good for us too.**

Ⓐ Fruits are good for us and so are green and yellow vegetables.

Ⓑ Fruits are good for us, and green vegetables and yellow vegetables.

Ⓒ Fruits are good for us and vegetables are too, green and yellow.

2 **Anke went horseback riding. She went out on the trail. It was early in the morning.**

Ⓕ Anke went on the trail early in the morning and she went horseback riding.

Ⓖ Early in the morning, Anke went horseback riding on the trail.

Ⓗ Anke went horseback riding and she went on the trail early in the morning.

Look at the fictitious website page for the search engine below. Then answer the questions on the next page. You may look back at this page as you answer the questions.

Name _____

1 **What is the purpose of a search engine?**

Ⓐ to sell parts for car engines

Ⓑ to update a website

Ⓒ to find website pages according to your search

Ⓓ to sign on to the Internet

2 **What is the name of this search engine?**

Ⓕ Web:

Ⓖ Explore!

Ⓗ Search.

Ⓙ Shortcut:

3 **What should you do to upgrade your virus protection while you are at this website page?**

Ⓐ click on the virus alert icon

Ⓑ call your computer company

Ⓒ click on Images

Ⓓ search the web for viruses

4 **If you would like to search for pictures of George Washington, which link would be best to use?**

Ⓕ Images

Ⓖ Directory

Ⓗ News

Ⓙ Favorites

Read the passage below. Then answer the questions on the next page. You may look back at this page as you answer the questions.

Practicing good manners simply means treating others as you would like to be treated.

When you want something, ask "May I..." and "Please."

When someone does something nice for you or gives you something, say "Thank you" or write a "thank you" letter.

If you do something to someone that you did not mean to do, quickly say "Excuse me" or "I'm sorry." The person who has been injured or who has hurt feelings may understand that you did not hurt them on purpose. Isn't it better that they understand and accept your apology rather than to strike back at you, seeking revenge?

If something you do makes a person angry, try to explain your actions. That may "take the wind out of their sails."

If you think you have been mistreated, insist quietly but firmly that you be treated with respect. You might say something like, "If you want me to treat you with respect, you must treat me with respect!"

At the table, eat quietly; no food fights! Use your napkin to keep your face clean. Having catsup on your chin is not very attractive.

Treating other people as you would like to be treated may help you earn more friends and more respect.

100

BELLWORK Reading/Language Arts • Level 5   © BELLWORK Enterprises – DO NOT DUPLICATE

Name _____

1 **Practicing good manners will —**

Ⓐ cause people to seek revenge
   against you.

Ⓑ hurt other people's feelings.

Ⓒ make you angry.

Ⓓ help you make friends.

2 **The author's *purpose* in writing this was —**

Ⓕ to entertain.

Ⓖ to advertise.

Ⓗ to write an autobiography.

Ⓙ to persuade.

3 **To "take the wind out of their sails" means —**

Ⓐ to make them angry.

Ⓑ to cause them to be less angry.

Ⓒ to earn their respect.

Ⓓ to hurt their feelings.

4 **To seek revenge means —**

Ⓕ to get even with someone.

Ⓖ to go backwards.

Ⓗ to echo.

Ⓙ to eat vegetables.

BELLWORK Reading/Language Arts • Level 5

Name _____

Fill in the bubble next to the answer that is punctuated correctly.

1 **Sung is an** _____ **boy.**

Ⓐ interesting smart and witty

Ⓑ interesting smart, and witty

Ⓒ interesting, smart, and witty

3 **Karen said,** _____

Ⓐ "Come in.

Ⓑ "Come in

Ⓒ "Come in."

2 **The date was** _____

Ⓕ October 12, 1492

Ⓖ October 12, 1492?

Ⓗ October 12, 1492.

4 _____ **was elected four times!**

Ⓕ President Franklin. D Roosevelt

Ⓖ President Franklin D Roosevelt

Ⓗ President Franklin D. Roosevelt

Name _____

Fill in the bubble in front of the contraction for the <u>underlined words</u>.

1 The baby <u>could</u> <u>not</u> tie her shoestrings.

Ⓐ can't
Ⓑ could'not
Ⓒ couldnt'
Ⓓ couldn't

2 This pen <u>will</u> <u>not</u> work.

Ⓕ wouldn't
Ⓖ willn't
Ⓗ won't
Ⓙ wont'

3 <u>She</u> <u>had</u> better come in out of the rain.

Ⓐ She'd
Ⓑ Shed
Ⓒ Sh'ed
Ⓓ Shed'

4 <u>We</u> <u>are</u> going shopping at the mall.

Ⓕ Were
Ⓖ Where
Ⓗ We're
Ⓙ Wer'e

103

Read the passage below. Then answer the questions on the next page. You may look back at this page as you answer the questions.

One Saturday morning, Paulina was trying to work on her state report. She was becoming very frustrated. She had gone to the library and checked out several books on different states. She had also researched a few of the states on the Internet. She had a lot of information, but she just couldn't decide which state to learn more about. Paulina wanted to do her report on three different states: Alaska, New York, and Virginia.

Paulina asked her parents for help in making a choice. Her mom suggested New York since there were a lot of interesting places to visit that she could write about. Her father suggested Virginia because that state had played a large role in the founding of the United States. Paulina just couldn't choose.

She finally decided to put each state's name on a piece of paper and draw one of the names from a basket. She drew Alaska! She couldn't wait to get started on her report.

Name _____

1 **In this passage the main problem or conflict is:**

Ⓐ Paulina has to do a state report.

Ⓑ Paulina can't decide which state to research for her report.

Ⓒ Paulina's parents won't help her.

Ⓓ School is difficult for Paulina.

2 **From the beginning to the end of the passage, how does Paulina's mood change?**

Ⓕ from sad to happy

Ⓖ from tired to energetic

Ⓗ from frustrated to excited

Ⓙ from angry to pleased

3 **Paulina resolves the problem by —**

Ⓐ deciding not to complete the report.

Ⓑ asking her teacher to help her choose.

Ⓒ doing her report on all three states.

Ⓓ selecting one of the state's names out of a basket.

4 **Which kind of character is Paulina?**

Ⓕ a smart student

Ⓖ a tough bully

Ⓗ a trusting friend

Ⓙ a helpful daughter

Name _____

Choose the answer that will form a complete sentence.

1 _____ caught the ball in his hand.

- Ⓐ Running
- Ⓑ In the outfield
- Ⓒ The umpire
- Ⓓ During the first inning

2 _____ needed to be replaced.

- Ⓕ At the typewriter
- Ⓖ The VCR
- Ⓗ Because of it
- Ⓙ Where the flag

3 _____ bought new athletic shoes.

- Ⓐ At the store
- Ⓑ My mother
- Ⓒ Brand new white
- Ⓓ Were too tight

4 _____ arrived in New York in the 1800s.

- Ⓕ From Europe
- Ⓖ Of the astronauts
- Ⓗ In 1799
- Ⓙ Many people from other countries

Name _____

Use the example below from a thesaurus to answer the questions that follow.

Rob used his thesaurus to find a synonym for <u>nervous</u>.

> **nervous** adj. edgy, fidgety, jittery, jumpy, restless, skittish. *See*: feelings. *Idioms*: all wound up, on edge, a bundle of nerves. (*Ant.*) calm, peaceful, serene.

Rob wrote the following sentence:

My dog, Scout, was <u>nervous</u> when he heard the loud bang.

❶ Which word should Rob use to replace the word <u>nervous</u> in the sentence?

Ⓐ feelings

Ⓑ calm

Ⓒ skittish

Ⓓ idiom

❷ Which word might Rob use as an antonym for <u>nervous</u>?

Ⓕ edgy

Ⓖ ant.

Ⓗ feelings

Ⓙ serene

❸ What other word(s) might Rob look up to find more synonyms for <u>nervous</u>?

Ⓐ peaceful

Ⓑ feelings

Ⓒ on edge

Ⓓ adj.

Name _____

Fill in the bubble next to the answer that correctly completes the sentence.

1 **I won't have _____ money until next week.**

(A) no

(B) any

2 **He doesn't _____ do his homework.**

(F) ever

(G) never

3 **It seems she doesn't like _____.**

(A) anybody

(B) nobody

4 **Jenna does not want _____ to eat.**

(F) nothing

(G) anything

5 **There wasn't _____ pizza left for me!**

(A) no

(B) any

6 **I don't like that kind of pizza _____.**

(F) no how

(G) no way

(H) anyway

Name _____

For each item below, choose the word that means *the same or almost the same* (synonym) as the <u>underlined word</u>.

1 <u>several</u> means —

   Ⓐ many
   Ⓑ few
   Ⓒ server
   Ⓓ sever

2 a <u>region</u> is —

   Ⓕ a reason
   Ⓖ a rule
   Ⓗ an area
   Ⓙ a religion

3 <u>got</u> means —

   Ⓐ govern
   Ⓑ go
   Ⓒ received
   Ⓓ give

4 <u>knock</u> means to —

   Ⓕ know
   Ⓖ knee
   Ⓗ kick
   Ⓙ rap

Name _____

❶ A metaphor is a literary device that —

Ⓐ compares three or more objects.

Ⓑ compares two things by stating that something is something else.

Ⓒ compares two things by using the words "as" or "like."

Ⓓ none of the above

❷ A simile is a literary device that —

Ⓕ compares three or more objects.

Ⓖ compares two things by stating that something is something else.

Ⓗ compares two things by using the words "as" or "like."

Ⓙ none of the above

❸ The sidewalk is as *slippery as ice*.

This is an example of a _____.

Ⓐ metaphor

Ⓑ simile

❹ We could have had more dessert if *Mauricio hadn't been such a hog*.

This is an example of a _____.

Ⓕ metaphor

Ⓖ simile

Name _____

Circle the word that is the *modifier*. Then underline the word that it is modifying.

1

She ran the track quickly.

2

John and Mike sat on a wooden bench.

3

Evelyn kicked the ball hard.

4

The paper was inadequate.

Read the passage below. Then answer the questions on the next page. You may look back at this page as you answer the questions.

"Wait a cotton-pickin' minute!" Perhaps you've heard that expression. However, from the time it's planted, you'd have to wait about six months to pick cotton. The next time you put on your blue jeans, see if they are made of cotton.

Cotton needs a lot of care during development from seeds to soft balls (bolls). Farmers must cultivate and fertilize the fields. They also treat the plants to avoid damage from disease and insects.

After many weeks in the hot sun, the cotton bolls are ready to be picked. Before the invention of mechanical pickers, cotton was always harvested by hand. It was backbreaking, hand-scratching work. People picking the cotton dragged it in heavy bags between rows of dry, thorny plants.

Modern harvesting machines pick the cotton and deposit it into a packer. The packer squeezes it into jute-covered bundles almost as big as railroad cars. Along the edges of the fields, those bundles look like huge loaves of bread.

The seeds still must be separated from the bolls in a cotton gin. After shipment to factories, the raw cotton can be made into fabric, perhaps for your blue jeans.

Name _____

1 **Cotton plants need —**

Ⓐ heavy bags.

Ⓑ little care.

Ⓒ cold weather.

Ⓓ lots of care.

2 **Mechanical pickers —**

Ⓕ press the cotton together.

Ⓖ are machines that pick cotton.

Ⓗ pick cotton by hand.

Ⓙ none of the above

3 **A cotton gin is used to —**

Ⓐ make jeans.

Ⓑ treat plants against insects.

Ⓒ separate the seeds from the bolls.

Ⓓ make fabric.

4 **Number the following in correct order.**

___ make cotton fabric

___ plant cotton seeds

___ separate the seeds from the bolls

___ pick the cotton bolls

113

Name _____

Use this index to choose the *best* answer to each question. Fill in the bubble.

Cats
    body, 104
    breeds, 106
    care, 107
    wild, 109

1 On what page would you find out whether or not to give your cat a bath?

Ⓐ 104   Ⓒ 107
Ⓑ 106   Ⓓ 109

2 On what page would you read about cats that are not pets?

Ⓕ 104   Ⓗ 108
Ⓖ 106   Ⓙ 109

3 On what page would you find a picture of the bone structure of a cat?

Ⓐ 107   Ⓒ 104
Ⓑ 108   Ⓓ 106

4 On what page might you find a picture of a Siamese cat?

Ⓕ 104   Ⓗ 105
Ⓖ 106   Ⓙ 108

Name _____

Read each set of sentences and decide if one of the <u>underlined words</u> is spelled *incorrectly*, or if there is *no mistake*. Choose your answer and fill in the bubble.

1

Ⓐ That water is not <u>puere</u>.
Ⓑ How tall is that <u>suspension</u> bridge in San Francisco?
Ⓒ I like to watch the <u>animals</u> play at the zoo.
Ⓓ no mistake

2

Ⓕ A magician <u>apeared</u> on TV.
Ⓖ You will <u>benefit</u> from your learning about math and science.
Ⓗ The software <u>application</u> froze and the computer would not respond.
Ⓙ no mistake

3

Ⓐ <u>Parrots</u> are good pets, if you don't mind the noise.
Ⓑ The adventurers saw <u>live</u> tigers.
Ⓒ Kareem missed the <u>parade</u> because he was on vacation.
Ⓓ no mistake

4

Ⓕ The travelers visited the <u>jungles</u> of Peru.
Ⓖ Who was the <u>sixteenth</u> President of the United States?
Ⓗ Do you like <u>strawberies</u> on your ice cream?
Ⓙ no mistake

115

Name _____

Mark the part of each sentence that needs a capital letter. If no capital is needed, mark "none."

1 Scott's apartment   is on   Hill street.   none
     Ⓐ   Ⓑ   Ⓒ   Ⓓ

2 His boss   is   mrs. Kim.   none
     Ⓕ   Ⓖ   Ⓗ   Ⓙ

3 The little man   was named   Tom hubbard.   none
     Ⓐ   Ⓑ   Ⓒ   Ⓓ

4 The year   begins   on New Year's Day.   none
     Ⓕ   Ⓖ   Ⓗ   Ⓙ

Name _____

Fill in the bubble under the <u>dependent clause</u>.

1 <u>Because she didn't complete her homework,</u> <u>she had to do it at recess</u>.
     Ⓐ   Ⓑ

2 <u>He didn't come to school</u> <u>because he was sick</u>.
     Ⓕ   Ⓖ

3 <u>While he was reading a book,</u> <u>his sister made a snack</u>.
     Ⓐ   Ⓑ

4 <u>She talked to her sister</u> <u>during the principal's speech</u>.
     Ⓕ   Ⓖ

Fill in the bubble under the <u>independent clause</u>.

5 <u>Because she didn't complete her homework,</u> <u>she had to do it at recess</u>.
     Ⓐ   Ⓑ

6 <u>He didn't come to school</u> <u>because he was sick</u>.
     Ⓕ   Ⓖ

7 <u>While he was reading a book,</u> <u>his sister made a snack</u>.
     Ⓐ   Ⓑ

8 <u>She talked to her sister</u> <u>during the principal's speech</u>.
     Ⓕ   Ⓖ

BELLWORK Reading/Language Arts • Level 5

Name _____

Read the following paragraph. Then choose the sentence that does _not_ belong.

Do you know what to do if you are caught in a burning building? Before opening a door, feel it with your hand. If it feels hot, you should probably try to find another way out. If there is a lot of smoke, a wet towel over your nose and mouth will help. Some hotels have elevators. You can get out more safely by crawling on the floor where there is less smoke and heat.

❶ Which sentence above does not belong?

Ⓐ Do you know what to do if you are caught in a burning building?

Ⓑ If it feels hot, you should probably try to find another way out.

Ⓒ Some hotels have elevators.

Ⓓ You can get out more safely by crawling on the floor where there is less smoke and heat.

Name _____

Use the dictionary entry to answer the questions below.

> **table** (tā´bəl) n. **1.** a collection of related items, a chart. **2.** a piece of furniture with a flat surface and with legs, used for serving food. **3.** a piece of furniture made for playing games. v. **4.** to lay aside or postpone.

Which of the above meanings fits each sentence below?

❶ **Please help me set the <u>table</u> for dinner.**

   Ⓐ Definition 1   Ⓒ Definition 3
   Ⓑ Definition 2   Ⓓ Definition 4

❷ **The committee <u>tabled</u> the question until their next meeting.**

   Ⓕ Definition 1   Ⓗ Definition 3
   Ⓖ Definition 2   Ⓙ Definition 4

❸ **Do you know your multiplication <u>tables</u>?**

   Ⓐ Definition 1   Ⓒ Definition 3
   Ⓑ Definition 2   Ⓓ Definition 4

❹ **Bring in the card <u>table</u>.**

   Ⓕ Definition 1   Ⓕ Definition 3
   Ⓖ Definition 2   Ⓒ Definition 4

119

Alex's teacher asked the class to write a story about a field trip. This is Alex's first draft. Read the story and then answer the questions on the next page.

1
The day had finally arrived! Today was the day of the 5th grade field trip to the observatory! I couldn't wait to get to the bus and leave. My class had been studying about the solar system, and I had turned in my planet project to Mrs. Andersen just yesterday!

2
As I was getting on the bus my stomach started to have a queasy feeling. As we drove down the freeway, the bouncing up and down made it even worse. I tried sitting in the front of the bus, but that didn't help either. My teacher gave me some water to drink. That helped my throat, but my stomach was still doing flips!

3
When we arrived at the observatory I stayed on the bus while the teachers decided what to do. After a few minutes my teacher got back on the bus and said, "Alex, we think it will be best if you go home with Mrs. Ryan in her car right away. We don't want you to stay here if you don't feel well." I was sad!

Name _____

1 **What was the setting for most of Alex's story?**

Ⓐ the school

Ⓑ a car

Ⓒ a school bus

Ⓓ his house

---

2 **If Alex wanted to further describe his upset stomach, he should add a sentence to paragraph —**

Ⓕ 1.

Ⓖ 2.

Ⓗ 3.

Ⓙ none of the above

3 **Which of these sentences should Alex add to the final paragraph to sum up his story?**

Ⓐ My teacher is mean.

Ⓑ My stomach was still sick.

Ⓒ I was in trouble at home.

Ⓓ I didn't get to go inside and see the observatory!

---

4 **Alex wants to use a different word for** <u>sad</u>. **He uses the thesaurus to find another word. Which word(s) would fit best in the sentence?**

Ⓕ miserable

Ⓖ cheerless

Ⓗ full of care

Ⓙ happy

Look at the timeline below. Then answer the questions on the following page. You may look back at this page as you answer the questions.

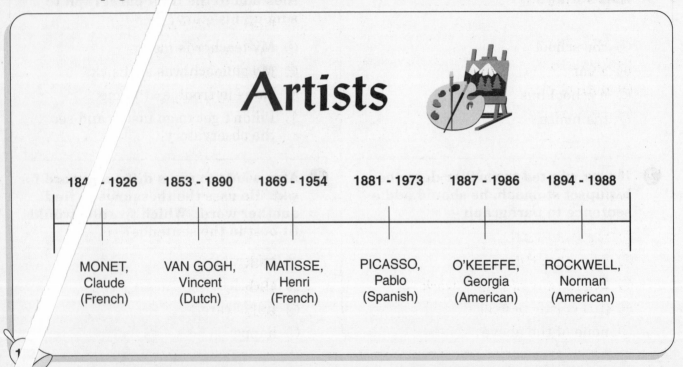

Artists

1840 - 1926	1853 - 1890	1869 - 1954	1881 - 1973	1887 - 1986	1894 - 1988
MONET, Claude (French)	VAN GOGH, Vincent (Dutch)	MATISSE, Henri (French)	PICASSO, Pablo (Spanish)	O'KEEFFE, Georgia (American)	ROCKWELL, Norman (American)

Name _____

1 **This timeline features artists ordered by their _____.**

Ⓐ first name
Ⓑ last name
Ⓒ date of birth
Ⓓ popularity

3 **Which artist was born in 1887?**

Ⓐ Norman Rockwell
Ⓑ Georgia O'Keeffe
Ⓒ Pablo Picasso
Ⓓ Henri Matisse

2 **The words in parentheses let us know _____.**

Ⓕ their nationality
Ⓖ where they died
Ⓗ where they did their work
Ⓙ their favorite food

4 **Each of these artists were born in which century?**

Ⓕ 17th
Ⓖ 18th
Ⓗ 19th
Ⓙ 20th

123

Name _____

Choose the word that will complete each sentence correctly.

1 I hope we have some _____ in our sandwiches.

Ⓐ meet   Ⓑ meat

4 Let's _____ for a minute and take a rest.

Ⓕ pause   Ⓖ paws

2 My mother's sister is my _____.

Ⓕ ant   Ⓖ aunt

5 The moon was bright last _____.

Ⓐ knight   Ⓑ night

3 The sun _____ brightly yesterday.

Ⓐ shone   Ⓑ shown

6 Shall I _____ a cup of water for you?

Ⓕ pour   Ⓖ poor

Name _____

Number each group of words in alphabetical order.

1
___ Sacramento
___ Springfield
___ Salem
___ Santa Fe

2
___ Cheyenne
___ Charleston
___ Columbia
___ Carson City

3
___ Phoenix
___ Providence
___ St. Paul
___ Pierre

4
___ Atlanta
___ Augusta
___ Annapolis
___ Albany

Name _____

Read each sentence. Fill in the bubble next to the words that make a <u>prepositional phrase</u>.

1 **Outside the yard, I could see children playing.**

Ⓐ Outside the yard
Ⓑ Outside the yard, I could see
Ⓒ I could see
Ⓓ I could see children playing

2 **Sean was swimming in the pond.**

Ⓕ Sean was
Ⓖ Sean was swimming
Ⓗ swimming in the pond
Ⓙ in the pond

3 **I could see three birds on the tree branch.**

Ⓐ I could see
Ⓑ I could see three birds
Ⓒ three birds on the tree branch
Ⓓ on the tree branch

4 **My grandfather was sitting on the recliner.**

Ⓕ My grandfather
Ⓖ grandfather was sitting
Ⓗ sitting on the recliner
Ⓙ on the recliner

Name _____

Use the mileage chart to answer the questions that follow.

	DESTINATION				
START LOCATION		Amarillo	Birmingham	Charleston	Dallas	Houston
Amarillo	—	967	1,265	358	596
Birmingham	967	—	552	645	639
Charleston	1,265	552	—	1,035	1,144
Dallas	358	645	1,035	—	243
Houston	596	639	1,144	243	—

1 Which two cities are the farthest from each other?

Ⓐ Birmingham and Amarillo

Ⓑ Amarillo and Charleston

Ⓒ Houston and Charleston

Ⓓ Houston and Dallas

2 Which two cities are the closest to each other?

Ⓕ Amarillo and Dallas

Ⓖ Charleston and Birmingham

Ⓗ Dallas and Amarillo

Ⓙ Houston and Dallas

3 If you traveled from Dallas to Charleston and then to Birmingham, how many miles would you travel altogether?

Ⓐ 1,035

Ⓑ 552

Ⓒ 1,587

Ⓓ 645

127

Name _____

Fill in the bubble next to the answer that correctly completes the sentence.

1 **They never do _____ right!**

Ⓐ anything

Ⓑ nothing

2 **There wasn't _____ at home.**

Ⓕ anybody

Ⓖ nobody

3 **Matthew could _____ find the Little Dipper.**

Ⓐ never

Ⓑ ever

4 **She won't ask for help from _____.**

Ⓕ no one

Ⓖ anyone

5 **I don't _____ want to hear you say that again!**

Ⓐ never

Ⓑ ever

6 **Tran didn't do _____ wrong.**

Ⓕ nothing

Ⓖ anything

128

Name _____

Fill in the bubble next to the answer that will form a complete sentence.

1

Ⓐ working all day
Ⓑ he works on the night shift
Ⓒ every day he
Ⓓ on the night shift

2

Ⓕ to the bank to get some
Ⓖ went to the bank to get some
Ⓗ she went to the bank to get some money
Ⓙ the bank to get some money

3

Ⓐ soprano singing in the chorus
Ⓑ singing in the chorus
Ⓒ in the chorus
Ⓓ the soprano sings in the chorus

4

Ⓕ she threw the paper on the porch
Ⓖ she threw
Ⓗ paper on the porch
Ⓙ on the porch

129

Name _____

Using the dictionary entry below, choose the *best* answer to each question.

---

an•to•nym (an´ · · nim) n.   a word directly opposite to another word in meaning.   [< Gk *anti-* opposite + *onyma* name]

---

1 An "antonym" is a word that —

Ⓐ has more than one meaning.

Ⓑ has an opposite meaning from another word.

Ⓒ is a boy's name.

2 The word "antonym" comes from —

Ⓕ the French language.

Ⓖ the Latin language.

Ⓗ the Greek language.

3 A person who is "antislavery" —

Ⓐ owns slaves.

Ⓑ is a slave.

Ⓒ is opposed to slavery.

4 If *pseudo* means false, a writer's <u>pseudonym</u> would be his —

Ⓕ real name.

Ⓖ fake name.

Ⓗ father's name.

Name _____

Read each sentence and look at the <u>underlined words</u>. There may be a mistake in them.
Select the best answer to correct the mistake. If there is no mistake, select *correct as is*.

---

❶ It <u>was a glorious sunset</u>.

Ⓐ was a gloriful sunset

Ⓑ was a gloried sunset

Ⓒ was a glory sunset

Ⓓ correct as is

---

❷ This book is <u>liking any book I have read</u>.

Ⓕ liked any book I have read

Ⓖ likeable any book I have read

Ⓗ unlike any book I have read

Ⓙ correct as is

---

❸ Our team <u>won the champions</u>.

Ⓐ won the champion

Ⓑ won the championship

Ⓒ won the championed

Ⓓ correct as is

---

❹ What she <u>said was unsense</u>.

Ⓕ said was nonsense

Ⓖ said was says

Ⓗ said was sensing

Ⓙ correct as is

Read the passage below. Then answer the questions on the next page. You may look back at this page as you answer the questions.

Do you want to be rich when you grow up? How do people become wealthy?

Some people <u>inherit</u> money or property when their parents or friends give it to them.

John D. Rockefeller, once the world's richest man, passed on his fortune to his children and to the public through the Rockefeller Foundation.

Henry Kaiser advised people to "Find a need and fill it." When his company was building ships for use in World War II, Kaiser started his own steel factories to supply the needed steel for his ships. In college, Bill Gates saw the need for new computer software to meet the special needs of large companies. From that beginning came the millions of personal computers in use today, and Bill Gates became a billionaire.

Working hard to develop their artistic and physical talents has helped some TV and movie stars and many professional athletes to become millionaires. Do you have a talent that you want to develop?

Many people place their savings in bank accounts or invest in businesses. That's another way to make your money grow. You could save small amounts of money every month from now until you retire. Including interest added over fifty or more years, you may have a surprisingly large amount. That would be nice, wouldn't it?

Name _____

1 The *main idea* of this passage is —

Ⓐ people become rich in different ways.

Ⓑ all rich people inherit money.

Ⓒ computer knowledge will make you wealthy.

Ⓓ ships are made of steel.

2 Henry Kaiser said —

Ⓕ "Build steel ships."

Ⓖ "Build factories to produce steel."

Ⓗ "World War II."

Ⓚ "Find a need and fill it."

3 The word <u>inherit</u> means —

Ⓐ Internet.

Ⓑ to receive from family or friends.

Ⓒ get it from her.

Ⓓ in the market.

4 Bill Gates —

Ⓕ developed oil wells.

Ⓖ was a newspaper man.

Ⓗ developed computer software.

Ⓚ played professional sports.

133

Name _____

Read the outline and the student composition written from the outline. Answer the question.

Texas
   I.   Location
   II. Size
   III. Products
   IV. History

   Texas is in the southern United States between New Mexico on the west, Oklahoma on the north and Louisiana and Arkansas on the east. When people think of Texas, pictures of cowboys and cattle sometimes come to mind. However, Texas has large supplies of gas and oil under its lands. Ranchers and farmers raise cattle and grow fruits, vegetables, and lots of cotton. At different times Texas belonged to Spain, France, and Mexico. It became a state in 1845, shortly before the Civil War.

1 **Choose the sentence needed to complete the composition according to the outline.**

  Ⓐ Texas is in the southern part of the United States.
  Ⓑ Cattle, oil, food crops, and cotton are produced in Texas.
  Ⓒ Texas is the second largest state in the United States.
  Ⓓ Texas joined the Union before the Civil War.

Name _____

Read each sentence and look at the underlined words. There may be a mistake in them. Select the best answer to correct the mistake. If there is no mistake, select *correct as is*.

1 **The teacher readed a book** to us.

Ⓐ The teacher red a book
Ⓑ The teacher read a book
Ⓒ The teacher reed a book
Ⓓ correct as is

2 **Alexander spent away** on his skates.

Ⓕ Alexander speeded away
Ⓖ Alexander rided away
Ⓗ Alexander sped away
Ⓙ correct as is

3 **The baby goed** to sleep.

Ⓐ The baby has went
Ⓑ The baby went
Ⓒ The baby is gone
Ⓓ correct as is

4 **My big brother has grew** up to be a man.

Ⓕ My big brother has growed
Ⓖ My big brother growed
Ⓗ My big brother grew
Ⓙ correct as is

135

Read the passage below. Then answer the questions on the next page. You may look back at this page as you answer the questions.

When you read the word <u>bow</u>, what do you think it means?
Do you think of a beautiful <u>bow</u> on top of a present?
Maybe you think of a musician or actor taking a <u>bow</u> after completing a performance. Have you ever seen a little girl wearing a <u>bow</u> in her hair? Have you seen the <u>bow</u> (front) of a ship? Do you know how far a <u>bow</u> can shoot an arrow?
Maybe you have seen someone using a <u>bow</u> to play a violin or cello.

How will you know which meaning of <u>bow</u> the author intended?

Read the entire sentence in which you find the word <u>bow</u>.
If you don't understand it, reread the sentence or the entire paragraph. More than likely, some other words in that sentence or paragraph will give you a clue as to the word's meaning. Figuring out whether <u>bow</u> is used as a noun or as a verb will give you another clue.

Name _____

Fill in the bubble next to the correct answer for question 1. Then fill in the bubble in front of the correct meaning of the word <u>bow</u> in questions 2, 3, and 4.

1 Her mother bought her a pretty pink <u>bow</u>. In this sentence, the word <u>bow</u> is a(n) —

Ⓐ noun.

Ⓑ adjective.

Ⓒ verb.

Ⓓ pronoun.

2 After the concert, the piano player came back on stage for a final <u>bow</u>. <u>Bow</u> means —

Ⓕ a ribbon on top of a gift.

Ⓖ a curve or bend.

Ⓗ to bend at the waist to acknowledge applause.

Ⓙ an object used to play a violin.

3 The hunter used his <u>bow</u> and arrow to hunt for the deer. <u>Bow</u> means —

Ⓐ to bend in respect.

Ⓑ the front part of a ship.

Ⓒ a sign with an arrow on it.

Ⓓ a strip of wood used to shoot arrows.

4 After I wrapped the present with paper, I attached a large, purple <u>bow</u>. <u>Bow</u> means —

Ⓕ something a dog barks.

Ⓖ a ribbon on top of a gift.

Ⓗ to bend at the waist to show respect.

Ⓙ a curve or bend.

Name _____

Fill in the bubble next to the answer that is punctuated correctly.

1 _____ wallet is on the table.

- Ⓐ Brandons
- Ⓑ Brandons'
- Ⓒ Brandon's

2 _____ she said.

- Ⓕ I'll be home then,
- Ⓖ "I'll be home then,"
- Ⓗ "I'll be home then,

3 I'll be home at _____.

- Ⓐ three oclock
- Ⓑ three oclock'
- Ⓒ three o'clock

4 The recipe calls for _____.

- Ⓕ milk flour, eggs, and vanilla
- Ⓖ milk, flour eggs and vanilla
- Ⓗ milk, flour, eggs, and vanilla

Name _____

Choose the answer that *best* combines the numbered sentences into *one sentence*.

1 They sat around a table. They played a game called Crazy Eights. Crazy Eights is a card game.

Ⓐ Crazy Eights is a card game, and they played around a table.

Ⓑ They sat around a table playing a card game called Crazy Eights.

Ⓒ They played a card game.

2 Thomas Jefferson designed his home. He founded the University of Virginia. Jefferson was our third President.

Ⓕ Thomas Jefferson designed his home called Monticello and founded the University of Virginia.

Ⓖ Thomas Jefferson designed his home and founded the University of Virginia, and he was our third President.

Ⓗ Thomas Jefferson, our third President, designed his home and founded the University of Virginia.

Name _____

Read the paragraph below. Then answer the questions that follow.

In a recent article on education, (Ohlson, 2003) the author found that struggling students need intensive intervention to succeed. This supported the research completed by Hernandez in 2000.

2 **The article by Ohlson was published in —**

Ⓕ 2030.

Ⓖ 2003.

Ⓗ 200.

Ⓙ 2000.

1 **To learn more about the article by Ohlson you would look at the —**

Ⓐ table of contents.

Ⓑ index.

Ⓒ bibliography.

Ⓓ title page.

3 **(Ohlson, 2003) is called —**

Ⓐ a footnote.

Ⓑ a citation.

Ⓒ an index.

Ⓓ none of the above

Name _____

Look at the advertisement below. Then answer the following questions.

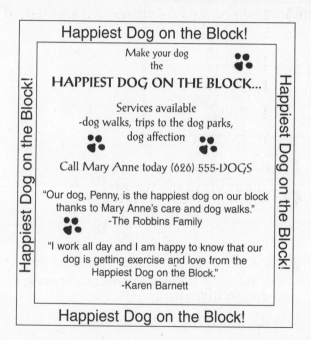

1. **Who is the target audience for this advertisement?**
   - (A) people who have time to walk their dogs
   - (B) people who don't have time to walk their dogs
   - (C) people who have time to walk their cats
   - (D) people who don't have a dog

2. **What persuasive devices does this advertisement use?**
   - (F) correct spelling
   - (G) phone numbers
   - (H) repetition and testimonials
   - (J) there are no persuasive devices

Name _____

Use the table of contents to answer each question. Fill in the bubble next to the *best* answer.

1 In this chapter, on what page would you find out the size of Earth?

Ⓐ 10   Ⓒ 12

Ⓑ 13   Ⓓ 14

2 On what page would you find out how scientists use telescopes?

Ⓕ 11   Ⓗ 12

Ⓖ 13   Ⓙ 14

3 On what page would you find out about Jupiter's moons?

Ⓐ 10   Ⓒ 11

Ⓑ 12   Ⓓ 13

4 On what page would you find out how long it takes Venus to travel around the Sun?

Ⓕ 10   Ⓗ 11

Ⓖ 12   Ⓙ 13

Name _____

Using the dictionary's *guide words*, fill in the bubble next to the word that would be defined on that page.

1 **bark** 25 **battery**

Ⓐ bandana   Ⓒ butter
Ⓑ base   Ⓓ battleship

3 **simple** 275 **siren**

Ⓐ sing   Ⓒ sky
Ⓑ silver Ⓓ six

2 **monk** 180 **moral**

Ⓕ Monday   Ⓗ morning
Ⓖ money   Ⓙ monkey

4 **first** 101 **flat**

Ⓕ float   Ⓗ fire
Ⓖ five   Ⓙ flatten

143

Name _____

Read the following paragraph. Then choose the sentence that does *not* belong.

Raul and Alfredo looked forward to playing with their new puppy. When they got home from school, they looked for the puppy. There was a swing hanging from the tree. They looked in the yard, but he was not there. They looked in the doghouse, but he was not there either. Then they found a hole in the dirt under the fence.

1 **Which sentence above does not belong?**

Ⓐ They looked in the doghouse, but he was not there either.

Ⓑ Raul and Alfredo looked forward to playing with their new puppy.

Ⓒ They looked in the yard, but he was not there.

Ⓓ There was a swing hanging from the tree.

Name _____

For each item below, choose the word that means *the same or almost the same* (synonym) as the <u>underlined word</u>.

❶ a <u>make-believe</u> story

Ⓐ real
Ⓑ truth
Ⓒ imaginary
Ⓓ journal

❷ a <u>gigantic</u> stadium

Ⓕ little
Ⓖ huge
Ⓗ small
Ⓙ laughing

❸ an <u>amazing</u> play

Ⓐ same
Ⓑ usual
Ⓒ ordinary
Ⓓ unusual

❹ a <u>swift</u> current

Ⓕ fast
Ⓖ slow
Ⓗ sweet
Ⓙ swinging

Read the passage below. Then answer the questions on the next page. You may look back at this page as you answer the questions.

"What is that big lump sticking up out of the water?" asked Steve.

"It looks like a great big fish," said Nathan. "Let's go down to the beach and see."

By the time the boys reached the ocean, the lifeguards were trying to get it back into deep water. However, every wave washed the creature farther up on shore.

The lifeguards asked the boys to help get the baby whale back into the water. They explained that whales are not really fish but mammals who breathe like we do but must be wet at all times. Besides, this baby still needed to be fed by its mother. The boys tried to help the lifeguards. However, the whale was firmly stuck and could not be moved, so Steve and Nathan splashed water on it. One of the lifeguards called for help from the marine biologists at Ocean Park.

These scientists, who work with whales every day, saw that the baby was too weak to swim back to its mother. They used their equipment to get this big mammal into a water-filled tank on their truck. Before leaving, they thanked everyone for helping to keep this special animal alive.

Still excited, Steve and Nathan ran home to tell their mother what had happened. Mother was very <u>proud</u> of her boys.

Name _____

1 **Mark the bubble next to the *best* statement for the plot of this passage.**

Ⓐ Steve and Nathan see a baby whale on the beach.

Ⓑ Marine biologists work with whales.

Ⓒ Steve and Nathan help save the life of a baby whale.

Ⓓ Lifeguards asked everyone to help.

2 **What was *unusual* about the whale in this passage?**

Ⓕ It swam in the ocean.

Ⓖ It needed help.

Ⓗ It could breathe like we do.

Ⓙ It traveled many miles.

3 **The setting of this passage is —**

Ⓐ Ocean Park.

Ⓑ Steve and Nathan's home.

Ⓒ the beach.

Ⓓ deep water.

4 **Mother was <u>proud</u> of her boys means that she —**

Ⓕ was sorry for them.

Ⓖ was angry with them.

Ⓗ was excited.

Ⓙ respected what they had done.

BELLWORK Reading/Language Arts • Level 5

Name _____

Read each sentence. Fill in the bubble next to the word(s) that is the <u>appositive</u>.

1 **Georgia O'Keeffe, my favorite artist, made several paintings of flowers.**

Ⓐ Georgia O'Keeffe
Ⓑ my favorite artist
Ⓒ made several paintings

2 **Polio, a disease from the early 1900s, paralyzed many Americans.**

Ⓕ Polio
Ⓖ a disease from the early 1900s
Ⓗ paralyzed many Americans

3 **Vegetables, especially green leafy ones, are good for your brain.**

Ⓐ Vegetables
Ⓑ especially green leafy ones
Ⓒ are good for your brain

4 **Milk, particularly chocolate, tastes good with cookies.**

Ⓕ Milk
Ⓖ particularly chocolate
Ⓗ tastes good with cookies

Name _____

Read and answer each question.

1 Which word suggests that Jim felt *angry*?

(A) glared

(B) looked

(C) stared

(D) eyed

2 Which word suggests that Jim felt *afraid*?

(F) grinned

(G) shook

(H) sneezed

(J) appeared

3 Which word suggests that Jim felt *sleepy*?

(A) smiled

(B) laughed

(C) coughed

(D) yawned

4 Which word suggests that Jim felt *proud*?

(F) upset

(G) slumped

(H) smiled

(J) sorry

Name _____

Read each sentence and look at the <u>underlined words</u>. There may be a mistake in them. Select the best answer to correct the mistake. If there is no mistake, select *correct as is*.

1 <u>Tom and me</u> like to take karate lessons.

 Ⓐ Tom and mine
 Ⓑ Tom and my
 Ⓒ Tom and I
 Ⓓ correct as is

2 Aunt Rosa takes <u>Margaret and I</u> to class.

 Ⓕ Margaret and we
 Ⓖ Margaret and me
 Ⓗ Margaret and she
 Ⓙ correct as is

3 <u>Us go to class</u> on Wednesday.

 Ⓐ We're go to class
 Ⓑ We go to class
 Ⓒ We've go to class
 Ⓓ correct as is

4 <u>I love to</u> dance.

 Ⓕ Us love to
 Ⓖ Them love to
 Ⓗ Me love to
 Ⓙ correct as is

Name _____

Fill in the bubble in front of the sentence that is worded correctly.

1

Ⓐ The choir sang softener.

Ⓑ The choir sang soft.

Ⓒ The choir sang softly.

2

Ⓕ Alaska is more colder than Hawaii.

Ⓖ Alaska is colder than Hawaii.

Ⓗ Alaska is coldest than Hawaii.

3

Ⓐ She listened more obedient.

Ⓑ She listened obedient.

Ⓒ She listened obediently.

4

Ⓕ This writing is the better you've ever done.

Ⓖ This writing is more better than you've ever done.

Ⓗ This writing is the best you've ever done.

Name _____

Choose the word that correctly completes each sentence.

1 The cow slowly _____ her cud.

    Ⓐ choose   Ⓑ chews

2 Will you _____ me some new jeans?

    Ⓕ buy   Ⓖ by

3 What is that _____ I smell?

    Ⓐ sent   Ⓑ scent

4 Our team _____ the soccer game.

    Ⓕ one   Ⓖ won

5 Jorge _____ and got the right answer.

    Ⓐ guest   Ⓑ guessed

6 It was _____ loss.

    Ⓕ their   Ⓖ there

Name _____

Fill in the bubble next to the answer that will make a complete sentence.

1 **The burnt toast** _____.

Ⓐ at the table
Ⓑ was too well-done
Ⓒ for breakfast
Ⓓ and eggs

2 **Penguins** _____.

Ⓕ live near cold water
Ⓖ the marine park
Ⓗ black and white
Ⓙ Antarctic

3 **Earthquakes** _____.

Ⓐ I'm afraid
Ⓑ in North America
Ⓒ night
Ⓓ shake the ground

4 **A tailor** _____.

Ⓕ in Hong Kong
Ⓖ can make clothing
Ⓗ experience
Ⓙ the clothing store

153

Dawn's teacher asked the class to write a short report on a business started in the United States. This is Dawn's first draft. Read the report and answer the questions on the next page.

1. The history of one hamburger restaurant is quite interesting. Two brothers ran a hamburger stand that sold hamburgers for 15 cents! They also used the Multimixer, a special five-spindle milkshake maker. The milkshakes were so popular that they actually used eight of the mixers in their restaurant.

2. In 1954 one man paid for the right to be the only person in the U.S. to distribute, or sell, the Multimixer. He visited the two brothers at their hamburger stand in California to convince them to open up several restaurants. He thought that if they opened more restaurants then they would buy more Multimixers from him! "Who could we get to open them for us?" one of the brothers asked.

3. "Well," the salesman answered, "I could do it."

4. The salesman opened his first hamburger restaurant in Des Plaines, Illinois in 1955. He made $366.12 the first day!

5. Imagine what would have happened if he had not traveled to California to try to sell these two brothers the Multimixer!

Name _____

1 Dawn went to the library to find a book on the history of hamburger restaurants. She found a book called *Famous Restaurants, Facts & Trivia*. Which part of the book discusses the history of hamburger restaurants?

- Ⓐ the table of contents
- Ⓒ the index
- Ⓑ the title page
- Ⓓ none of the above

2 Which sentence defines the topic for the report?

- Ⓕ The history of one hamburger restaurant is quite interesting.
- Ⓖ The brothers ran a hamburger stand that sold hamburgers for 15 cents!
- Ⓗ "Well," the salesman answered, "I could do it."
- Ⓙ He made $366.12 the first day!

3 Which sentence could be added to paragraph 4?

- Ⓐ The Multimixer made shakes very quickly.
- Ⓑ The salesman was 52 years old.
- Ⓒ Before selling Multimixers, the salesman sold real estate and paper cups.
- Ⓓ This restaurant is now a museum containing restaurant memorabilia.

4 One reason this report is nonfiction is that —

- Ⓕ it contains true facts about hamburger restaurants.
- Ⓖ it is written in simple language.
- Ⓗ it happened in the past.
- Ⓙ the words rhyme.

BELLWORK Reading/Language Arts • Level 5

Read the passage below. Then answer the questions on the next page. You may look back at this page as you answer the questions.

A genius has unusual talent to do something very, very well. If you are a genius with one special interest, perhaps you should put all your energies into that one activity. But if you are like most people, perhaps you should develop all your interests and talents as far as possible. One never knows what <u>avenues</u> may open in the future.

In elementary school, Bill Johnson decided he wanted to be a teacher. Later, as his musical abilities improved, he decided to teach music.

However, in high school everybody had to take a computer course. Bill enjoyed computers more than he had imagined. In college, he continued with computer classes. This knowledge came in very handy. He could write papers and send them to his professor by modem. He could e-mail letters to his parents without paying for long-distance telephone calls.

When Bill applied for a teaching position, there was no opening for a music teacher. There was a job for a teacher of computers! Mr. Johnson still enjoyed music and also enjoyed his position as a teacher of computer skills.

Name _____

1 **A genius has —**

Ⓐ a lot of talent.
Ⓑ no talent.
Ⓒ a magic lamp.
Ⓓ little sense.

2 **Mr. Johnson always wanted —**

Ⓕ to write letters.
Ⓖ to learn computers.
Ⓗ to teach.
Ⓙ to write papers.

3 **In paragraph one the word <u>avenues</u> means —**

Ⓐ streets.
Ⓑ roads.
Ⓒ chances to do something.
Ⓓ the future.

4 **From this passage you can tell that it is a good idea to —**

Ⓕ be handy.
Ⓖ teach music.
Ⓗ develop more than one interest or talent.
Ⓙ know the future.

157

Name _____

Read each sentence and look at the underlined words. There may be a mistake in them. Select the best answer to correct the mistake. If there is no mistake, select *correct as is*.

1 We have <u>twenty-five problems</u> for homework.

   Ⓐ twenty-five problem

   Ⓑ twenty-five problemes

   Ⓒ twenty-five problemies

   Ⓓ correct as is

2 Elizabeth's uncle has <u>two riding horsses</u>.

   Ⓕ two riding horse

   Ⓖ two riding horsies

   Ⓗ two riding horses

   Ⓙ correct as is

3 They looked at <u>two gold watch</u>.

   Ⓐ two gold watchs

   Ⓑ two gold watchies

   Ⓒ two gold watches

   Ⓓ correct as is

4 We were given <u>three different calendars</u> for the new year.

   Ⓕ three different calendar

   Ⓖ three different calendares

   Ⓗ three different calendarys

   Ⓙ correct as is

Name _____

Use the reference citation below to answer the questions that follow.

Burrows, C. L. (2005). Helping low achieving students meet the standards. <u>National Education 52</u>, 189–196.

2 The article is found on page(s) _____ of the journal.

Ⓕ 2005

Ⓖ 52

Ⓗ 189–196

1 The title of the article is —

Ⓐ Burrows, C. L.

Ⓑ Helping low achieving students meet the standards.

Ⓒ National Education.

3 The article was published in which journal?

Ⓐ Burrows, C. L.

Ⓑ Helping low achieving students meet the standards

Ⓒ National Education

Name _____

Fill in the bubble next to the correct answer.

1 In the word <u>non</u>sense, the "non–" makes the word mean —

Ⓐ scents.

Ⓑ no sense.

Ⓒ sensed again.

Ⓓ more sensible.

2 In the word <u>re</u>told, the "re–" makes the word mean —

Ⓕ not told.

Ⓖ told across.

Ⓗ told to.

Ⓙ told again.

3 In the word <u>de</u>part, the "de–" makes the word mean —

Ⓐ part from.

Ⓑ part of.

Ⓒ part again.

Ⓓ not parting.

4 In the word <u>un</u>fortunate, the "un–" makes the word mean —

Ⓕ very fortunate.

Ⓖ in a fortunate manner.

Ⓗ not fortunate.

Ⓙ most fortunate.

Name _____

Fill in the bubble next to the antonym of each <u>underlined word</u>.

1 The *opposite* of <u>dangerous</u> is —

Ⓐ perilous.
Ⓑ unsafe.
Ⓒ safe.
Ⓓ dancing.

2 The *opposite* of <u>north</u> is —

Ⓕ east.
Ⓖ northern.
Ⓗ west.
Ⓙ south.

3 The *opposite* of <u>shout</u> is —

Ⓐ yell.
Ⓑ whisper.
Ⓒ tell.
Ⓓ say.

4 The *opposite* of <u>closed</u> is —

Ⓕ open.
Ⓖ clothes.
Ⓗ lock.
Ⓙ shut.

161

Name _____

Choose the word (conjunction) that *best* connects the thoughts in each of the following sentences.

1 The bus brought us to school, _____ it will take us home.

  Ⓐ nor   Ⓒ and

  Ⓑ but   Ⓓ because

2 Yosemite Park will be very crowded, _____ our family has made reservations.

  Ⓕ for   Ⓗ because

  Ⓖ but   Ⓙ or

3 Guam gets neither snow _____ icy weather.

  Ⓐ nor   Ⓒ as

  Ⓑ but   Ⓓ until

4 The cowboy was aware of the danger _____ full of courage.

  Ⓕ or   Ⓗ yet

  Ⓖ either   Ⓙ for

Name _____

After reading the three lines below, fill in the bubbles in front of the correct answers.

On black velvet skies
Between white cotton cloud puffs
Millions of diamonds.

1 The three lines, called "haiku," are a form of —

Ⓐ drama.　　　　Ⓒ poetry.

Ⓑ fable.　　　　Ⓓ biography.

3 In this haiku, the author is thinking about —

Ⓐ fabric.　　　　Ⓒ the wind.

Ⓑ jewelry.　　　　Ⓓ stars.

2 The first two lines indicate that the night feels —

Ⓕ soft.　　　　Ⓗ hot.

Ⓖ cold.　　　　Ⓙ hard.

4 The last line indicates —

Ⓕ baseball.　　　　Ⓗ money.

Ⓖ lights.　　　　Ⓙ snakes.

Name _____

❶ Fill in the bubble next to the sentence that contains a metaphor.

Ⓐ Adriana is a mule and we couldn't get her to change her mind.

Ⓑ The poster glows in the dark.

Ⓒ The water is very cold.

Ⓓ Sam is as sharp as a tack.

---

❷ *Savannah is a chicken. She won't even ride her bike without the training wheels.*

This metaphor compares Savannah to a chicken because —

Ⓕ she has feathers.

Ⓖ she will try anything.

Ⓗ she is as smart as a chicken.

Ⓙ she is afraid.

❸ *Debbie is a volcano. She gets mad and yells each time I ask a question.*

This metaphor compares Debbie to a volcano because —

Ⓐ she is a nice person.

Ⓑ she is patient.

Ⓒ she has a bad temper.

Ⓓ she is a lazy girl.

---

❹ The metaphor *Debbie is a volcano,* **creates a feeling of _____.**

Ⓕ hope

Ⓖ anger

Ⓗ sadness

Ⓙ joy

Name _____

Circle the word that is the *modifier*. Then underline the word that it is modifying.

1

The child was honest.

2

Tracy read books quietly.

3

Kim walked quickly to the park.

4

The dog was friendly.

Name _____

Using the encyclopedia pictured below, fill in the bubble next to the correct answer.

1 In which volume could you learn how to train a horse?

Ⓐ 3   Ⓒ 5

Ⓑ 6   Ⓓ 13

2 In which volume could you learn about a man named Peter Sendak?

Ⓕ 5   Ⓗ 6

Ⓖ 8   Ⓙ 12

3 In which <u>two</u> volumes might you find out about diving for pearls?

Ⓐ 3 and 10   Ⓒ 1 and 10

Ⓑ 6 and 10   Ⓓ 10 and 11

4 In which volume would you find the history of clocks?

Ⓕ 3   Ⓗ 4

Ⓖ 5   Ⓙ 6

Name _____

Read each sentence and look at the <u>underlined words</u>. There may be a mistake in them. Select the best answer to correct the mistake. If there is no mistake, select *correct as is*.

1 <u>**She taught us**</u> **a new way to do equations.**

Ⓒ She teached us

Ⓓ She teach us

Ⓔ She taughted us

Ⓕ correct as is

2 <u>**Did you forgetting how to**</u> **do that math problem?**

Ⓝ Did you forget how to

Ⓞ Did you forgot how to

Ⓟ Did you forgotten how to

Ⓤ correct as is

3 <u>**Last night, the soldiers stand**</u> **at attention to salute the flag.**

Ⓒ Last night, the soldiers standed

Ⓓ Last night, the soldiers stood

Ⓔ Last night, the soldiers standing

Ⓕ correct as is

4 **I am glad** <u>**he will drove me**</u> **to the game.**

Ⓝ he will driven me

Ⓞ he will driving me

Ⓟ he will drive me

Ⓤ correct as is

167

Name _____

Mark the part of each sentence that needs a capital letter. If no capital is needed, mark "none."

1 <u>Over the weekend</u>   <u>we went</u>   <u>to Sea Life park</u>.   none
     Ⓐ   Ⓑ   Ⓒ   Ⓓ

2 <u>They went</u>   <u>to church</u>   <u>on New Year's eve</u>.   none
     Ⓕ   Ⓖ   Ⓗ   Ⓙ

3 <u>We saw</u>   <u>dr. Merchant</u>   <u>yesterday</u>.   none
     Ⓐ   Ⓑ   Ⓒ   Ⓓ

4 <u>Courtney's birthday</u>   <u>is</u>   <u>May 6</u>.   none
     Ⓕ   Ⓖ   Ⓗ   Ⓙ

Name _____

Mark the bubble next to the word that will fit in <u>both</u> sentences.

1 Han _____ with a loud voice, "Help, the house is on fire!"
The movie was so sad that she _____ many tears.

Ⓐ said
Ⓑ cried
Ⓒ shed
Ⓓ yelled

2 The garden was planted in a small _____ of ground.
She needs to _____ the hole in her blue jeans.

Ⓕ cloth
Ⓖ square
Ⓗ fix
Ⓙ patch

3 The pirates found a treasure _____.
I have a pain in my _____.

Ⓐ leg
Ⓑ neck
Ⓒ map
Ⓓ chest

4 Julie's father _____ an accident.
The carpenter used a hammer and a _____.

Ⓕ caused
Ⓖ saw
Ⓗ nail
Ⓙ drill

Name _____

Read each set of sentences and decide if one of the <u>underlined words</u> is spelled *incorrectly*, or if there is *no mistake*. Choose your answer and fill in the bubble.

 1

Ⓐ Mother said it was the <u>write</u> thing to do.

Ⓑ <u>Eight</u> houses were destroyed by the tornado.

Ⓒ That star is a <u>million</u> miles away.

Ⓓ no mistake

 2

Ⓕ That movie was filled with <u>action</u>.

Ⓖ We played soccer in the <u>pouring</u> rain on Friday.

Ⓗ Caroline is my <u>cousun</u>.

Ⓙ no mistake

 3

Ⓐ Our school is opening up a new <u>cafeteria</u> in the fall.

Ⓑ Derek is <u>capten</u> of the team.

Ⓒ The hockey stick broke into two <u>pieces</u> on the ice.

Ⓓ no mistake

 4

Ⓕ The teacher says I need to <u>practice</u> my handwriting.

Ⓖ You were lucky to win that <u>prize</u>.

Ⓗ I am meeting them at the café for <u>breckfast</u>.

Ⓙ no mistake

Name _____

Read this composition and answer the question that follows.

Our writing paper is made mostly from trees. A lot of trees have to be cut down to make paper. The paper we use in school may be recycled. When old newspapers, computer paper, grocery bags, and other waste papers are recycled, they are cleaned and made into paper pulp, and then processed into paper again.

1 **What suggestion would you make to the student who wrote this?**

Ⓐ Describe your favorite tree.

Ⓑ Tell about the effects of cutting trees to make paper.

Ⓒ Describe your writing paper.

Ⓓ Tell what newspaper you take.

Read the selection below. Then answer the questions on the next page. You may look back at this page as you answer the questions.

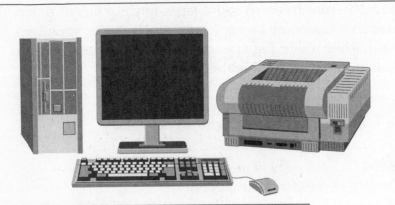

SAVE 25% TODAY

Our computer system comes complete with a 2.0 GHz Processor, 20 inch Flat Panel Display, Laser Printer, and 40 software programs already installed!

Store hours:
Mon - Fri 8AM - 8PM
Sat - Sun 10AM - 6PM

Communication Technology, Inc.
Seattle
1010 Silicon Valley Street (101) 101-1010

Name _____

1 **Choose the author's _purpose_ in writing the previous page.**

Ⓐ to entertain
Ⓑ to sell
Ⓒ to teach
Ⓓ to buy

2 **The advertisement says that —**

Ⓕ you should start running.
Ⓖ the store is open 24 hours a day.
Ⓗ the store is in Silicon Valley.
Ⓙ you can save 25%.

3 **The word "software" means —**

Ⓐ soft cloths.
Ⓑ dinner napkins.
Ⓒ programs for computers.
Ⓓ quiet conflict.

4 **The computer comes with —**

Ⓕ a flat panel and printer only.
Ⓖ sound equipment.
Ⓗ a flat panel, printer, and software.
Ⓙ a scanner.

Name _____

Fill in the bubble next to the word that correctly completes each sentence.

1 The word <u>should</u> is *closest in meaning to* —

Ⓐ shout.

Ⓑ shall.

Ⓒ show.

Ⓓ short.

2 The word <u>left</u> is *closest in meaning to* —

Ⓕ right.

Ⓖ leaf.

Ⓗ leave.

Ⓙ swift.

3 The word <u>would</u> is *closest in meaning to* —

Ⓐ will.

Ⓑ wool.

Ⓒ wood.

Ⓓ wound.

4 The word <u>came</u> is *closest in meaning to* —

Ⓕ same.

Ⓖ come.

Ⓗ cane.

Ⓙ ran.

Name _____

Fill in the bubble under the *simple subject*.

1 <u>Many white</u>   <u>geese</u>   <u>swam</u>   <u>downstream</u>.
   Ⓐ   Ⓑ   Ⓒ   Ⓓ

2 <u>Some fast-food</u>   <u>businesses</u>   <u>are</u>   <u>very</u>
   Ⓕ   Ⓖ   Ⓗ   Ⓙ
<u>profitable</u>.
   Ⓚ

3 <u>The whole</u>   <u>family</u>   <u>went</u>   <u>to the park</u>.
   Ⓐ   Ⓑ   Ⓒ   Ⓓ

4 <u>He</u>   <u>is</u>   <u>a good friend</u>.
   Ⓕ Ⓖ   Ⓗ

Fill in the bubble under the *simple predicate*.

5 <u>Many white</u>   <u>geese</u>   <u>swam</u>   <u>downstream</u>.
   Ⓐ   Ⓑ   Ⓒ   Ⓓ

6 <u>Some fast-food</u>   <u>businesses</u>   <u>are</u>   <u>very</u>
   Ⓕ   Ⓖ   Ⓗ   Ⓙ
<u>profitable</u>.
   Ⓚ

7 <u>The whole</u>   <u>family</u>   <u>went</u>   <u>to the park</u>.
   Ⓐ   Ⓑ   Ⓒ   Ⓓ

8 <u>He</u>   <u>is</u>   <u>a good friend</u>.
   Ⓕ Ⓖ   Ⓗ

175

Name _____

Using the prefix **trans-** and the dictionary entry, choose the *best* answer to each question.

> **trans•con•ti•nen•tal** (trans′ · kon · tə · nen′ · təl) adj.   extending or going across a continent.

❶ What is the farthest distance a <u>transcontinental</u> railroad goes?

Ⓐ through California

Ⓑ across Chicago

Ⓒ clear across the continent

❷ If a pilot is on a <u>transoceanic</u> flight, the plane flies —

Ⓕ over Asia.

Ⓖ across the ocean.

Ⓗ through thick clouds.

❸ If a patient has a blood <u>transfusion</u>, the blood goes —

Ⓐ from one source to another.

Ⓑ through a fuse.

Ⓒ across a continent.

❹ If a product is <u>transportable</u>, that means it can be —

Ⓕ carried from one place to another.

Ⓖ passed through a table.

Ⓗ put over a porthole.

Name _____

Fill in the bubble next to the correct answer.

1 **In the word hard<u>en</u>, the "–en" makes the word mean —**

Ⓐ one who makes something hard.

Ⓑ not easy.

Ⓒ to make hard.

Ⓓ soft.

2 **In the word <u>trans</u>atlantic, the "trans–" makes the word mean —**

Ⓕ in the ocean.

Ⓖ not the Atlantic.

Ⓗ across the Atlantic.

Ⓙ the Atlantic.

3 **In the word <u>sub</u>marine, the "sub–" makes the word mean —**

Ⓐ over water.

Ⓑ underwater ship.

Ⓒ in the service.

Ⓓ a sandwich.

4 **In the word <u>inter</u>state, the "inter–" makes the word mean —**

Ⓕ not stated.

Ⓖ understood.

Ⓗ between the states.

Ⓙ in the state.

Name _____

Fill in the bubble next to the sentence that is punctuated correctly.

1
Ⓐ The clock read 10:35 - it was time for recess.

Ⓑ The clock read 1:035 - it was time for recess.

Ⓒ The clock read 103:5 - it was time for recess.

Ⓓ The clock read 1035 - it was time for recess.

2
Ⓕ The teacher said we could have a snack at 1105.

Ⓖ The teacher said we could have a snack at 1:105.

Ⓗ The teacher said we could have a snack at 110:5.

Ⓙ The teacher said we could have a snack at 11:05.

3
Ⓐ I have three favorite fruits apples, pears, and peaches.

Ⓑ I have three favorite fruits apples,: pears, and peaches.

Ⓒ I have three favorite fruits: apples, pears, and peaches.

Ⓓ I have three favorite: fruits apples, pears, and peaches.

4
Ⓕ Marian likes only one color: blue.

Ⓖ Marian likes only one: color blue.

Ⓗ Marian: likes only one color blue.

Ⓙ Marian likes only one color blue.

Name _____

Fill in the bubble next to the verb that correctly completes each sentence.

1 Father _____ in his favorite chair.

Ⓐ sit

Ⓑ sits

2 He _____ the sheets and towels.

Ⓕ were drying

Ⓖ was drying

3 Mom _____ a good book to us.

Ⓐ is reading

Ⓑ are reading

4 The children _____ to the teacher.

Ⓕ is listening

Ⓖ are listening

5 The waiters _____ their hands.

Ⓐ washes

Ⓑ wash

6 Olivia and Abby _____ on a train.

Ⓕ have ridden

Ⓖ has ridden

179

Read the passage below. Then answer the questions on the next page. You may look back at this page as you answer the questions.

When she visited her mother in a nursing home, Mrs. Locke saw that many residents (patients) never had visitors. Some had relatives, but they lived too far away to visit. Some had no relatives, and their friends had stopped coming to see them.

Mrs. Locke decided to organize a group of people who would visit several patients once every two weeks. She asked Mrs. Ito, but she just didn't have the time. Mrs. Floyd said she didn't like being around sick people. Ms. Birch said her fifth grade class could visit before the holidays. They could sing or do little plays for the patients. However, they couldn't take the time off from school to visit more often.

Finally, six men and women joined the group. They called themselves "The Visitors Club." Each member would visit several patients. For some of the patients, the visitor could just hold their hand and try to comfort them. Other residents wanted to talk with the visitors about things that were happening in the outside world. Some older people chatted about their lives before they had become disabled. All of them were grateful to see the friendly, smiling faces of their visitors. They looked forward to the days when the folks from The Visitors Club would come again.

Name _____

1 From this passage you can tell that some of the patients —

Ⓐ were healthy.

Ⓑ could sing.

Ⓒ were lonely.

Ⓓ could dance.

3 People from The Visitors Club were _____ to the residents.

Ⓐ kind

Ⓑ mean

Ⓒ unpleasant

Ⓓ rude

2 The purpose of The Visitors Club was —

Ⓕ to see their relatives.

Ⓖ to play cards.

Ⓗ to advertise.

Ⓙ to bring pleasure to the residents.

4 People from The Visitors Club went to the nursing home —

Ⓕ every seven days.

Ⓖ every fourteen days.

Ⓗ only before holidays.

Ⓙ every other day.

181

Name _____

Choose the word that *best* connects the thoughts in each of the following sentences. Then *write* each new sentence on the line provided. Add punctuation where necessary.

1 **I heard him speak. I didn't like what he said.**

Ⓐ unless   Ⓑ although   Ⓒ whether   Ⓓ or

_____

2 **The pencil lead is okay. The eraser is worn out.**

Ⓕ whether   Ⓖ because   Ⓗ so   Ⓘ but

_____

3 **It's Valentine's Day. Tell someone "I love you."**

Ⓐ for   Ⓑ or   Ⓒ so   Ⓓ either

_____

Name _____

Read each sentence and look at the <u>underlined words</u>. There may be a mistake in them. Select the best answer to correct the mistake. If there is no mistake, select *correct as is*.

---

1 Look at <u>Zacharys' new in-line skates!</u>

   Ⓐ Zacharys new in-line skates!

   Ⓑ Zacharies new in-line skates!

   Ⓒ Zachary's new in-line skates!

   Ⓓ correct as is

---

2 We need <u>a lot of packing boxs'.</u>

   Ⓕ a lot of packing boxs.

   Ⓖ a lot of packing boxes.

   Ⓗ a lot of packing box's.

   Ⓙ correct as is

---

3 A pair of gloves would keep <u>my hands</u> warm.

   Ⓐ my handes

   Ⓑ my hand's

   Ⓒ my hands'

   Ⓓ correct as is

---

4 Mother said, "<u>Its' time for bed</u> now."

   Ⓕ "Its time for bed

   Ⓖ "It's time for bed

   Ⓗ "It time for bed

   Ⓙ correct as is

183

Name _____

Fill in the bubble next to the word that correctly completes each sentence.

1 All _____ have three wheels.

   Ⓐ motorcycles

   Ⓑ unicycles

   Ⓒ bicycles

   Ⓓ tricycles

2 He had a _____ part in the play.

   Ⓕ speak

   Ⓖ speaker

   Ⓗ nonspeaking

   Ⓙ speechless

3 Her room was messy and _____.

   Ⓐ unclean

   Ⓑ cleaning

   Ⓒ reclean

   Ⓓ neat

4 That airplane part is _____.

   Ⓕ repairing

   Ⓖ disrepair

   Ⓗ unrepairable

   Ⓙ repair

Name _____

Fill in the bubble next to the word (article) that correctly completes each sentence.

1 Hand me _____ crayon from that box, please.

Ⓐ a

Ⓑ an

2 Ryan likes cheese on _____ ham sandwich.

Ⓕ a

Ⓖ an

3 Mai has _____ orange for lunch.

Ⓐ a

Ⓑ an

4 Did you get _____ ice-cream bar?

Ⓕ a

Ⓖ an

5 I need _____ straw for my milk.

Ⓐ a

Ⓑ an

6 I chose _____ cupcake.

Ⓕ a

Ⓖ an

Read the passage below. Then answer the questions on the next page. You may look back at this page as you answer the questions.

Years ago, people on Catalina Island would send a grocery order in a pouch fastened to a "carrier" pigeon's leg band or its back. The next day the food would be delivered by boat. Pigeons have been used to carry important messages in wartime too. With modern methods of communication, pigeons are no longer used by the army.

Unlike wild birds, domestic pigeons are raised and cared for by people at <u>their</u> homes. Homing pigeons fly back to their loft from different places. They can find their way home from a distance of 600 or more miles. (Some people think the birds may use the magnetic pull of the earth or the position of the sun to find their way home.)

Pigeons can fly as fast as sixty miles an hour. Some people race their birds to see which ones are the fastest.

Many different breeds of pigeons are raised for showing. At a pigeon show, a bird with beautiful feathers, a crested head, a ruff of feathers around its neck, or red feathers on its chest may win a prize for its owner.

Pigeons can be raised for food. It doesn't take much room to raise pigeons. The meat is called squab.

Name _____

1 The *main idea* of this passage is —

Ⓐ all pigeons are wild.

Ⓑ domestic birds are fast fliers.

Ⓒ domestic pigeons are used in many ways.

Ⓓ pigeons can fly fast.

2 Is it *fact* or *opinion* that homing pigeons are beautiful?

Ⓕ fact

Ⓖ opinion

3 The word <u>their</u> in paragraph two refers to —

Ⓐ birds.

Ⓑ people.

Ⓒ cities.

Ⓓ diseases.

4 Some pigeons are called "carrier" pigeons because —

Ⓕ they live on aircraft carriers.

Ⓖ they carry diseases.

Ⓗ they carry messages.

Ⓙ they are carried far away.

187

Name _____

Fill in the bubble next to the *best* source of information.

1 To find a list of all the books about earthquakes, look in —

Ⓐ a newspaper.

Ⓑ a telephone directory.

Ⓒ a library's computer.

Ⓓ an atlas.

2 To find the phone number of the post office in your city, look in —

Ⓕ a dictionary.

Ⓖ a telephone directory.

Ⓗ an atlas.

Ⓙ an almanac.

3 To find a map showing the Amazon River, look in —

Ⓐ an almanac.

Ⓑ a dictionary.

Ⓒ a glossary.

Ⓓ an atlas.

4 To find the time of low tide, look in —

Ⓕ a dictionary.

Ⓖ an almanac.

Ⓗ a table of contents.

Ⓙ an index.

Name _____

Fill in the bubble next to the correct answer.

1 **Where, in most books, is the *index* found?**

    Ⓐ on the title page
    Ⓑ in the front
    Ⓒ at the back
    Ⓓ on the cover

2 **It is easier to find the exact page on which a topic is covered in the —**

    Ⓕ glossary.
    Ⓖ table of contents.
    Ⓗ index.

3 **An *index* tells —**

    Ⓐ page numbers where topics are found.
    Ⓑ who wrote the book.
    Ⓒ how many pages are in the book.
    Ⓓ the names of the chapters.

4 **Which marking below shows that information continues for several pages in a row (next to each other)?**

    Ⓕ 1, 3, 44
    Ⓖ 1–3

189

Name _____

Fill in the bubble under the *simple predicate* in each sentence.

On the line under each sentence, write its *complete predicate*.

1 The whistle blew loudly.
    Ⓐ   Ⓑ   Ⓒ   Ⓓ

5 The whistle blew loudly.

_____

2 Sophia and I bought new shoes.
    Ⓕ   Ⓖ   Ⓗ   Ⓙ

6 Sophia and I bought new shoes.

_____

3 The old car ran a red light.
    Ⓐ   Ⓑ   Ⓒ   Ⓓ

7 The old car ran a red light.

_____

4 Jack-o'-lanterns glow on Halloween.
    Ⓕ   Ⓖ   Ⓗ

8 Jack-o'-lanterns glow on Halloween.

_____

Name _____

Choose the word that will correctly complete each sentence.

1 Cary is his father's _____.

   Ⓐ son   Ⓑ sun

2 When will we get _____ report cards?

   Ⓕ hour   Ⓖ our

3 Lupe _____ how to multiply.

   Ⓐ nose   Ⓑ knows

4 May I have another _____ of pie?

   Ⓕ piece   Ⓖ peace

5 These shirts are _____ big.

   Ⓐ two   Ⓑ too

6 I read the _____ story last night.

   Ⓕ whole   Ⓖ hole

Read the passage below. Then answer the questions on the next page. You may look back at this page as you answer the questions.

A peninsula is a long finger of land almost surrounded by water.

Florida, with the waters of the Atlantic Ocean on the east and the Gulf of Mexico on its west, is sometimes called the "Peninsula State." It is joined to Georgia on the north and Alabama on the north and west. Florida's coastline is 1,350 miles long and provides good fishing. Because of its warm temperatures and frequent rains, many crops grow well on most of Florida's almost 60,000 square miles. Lots of people visit its tourist attractions, and many older people like to retire in its warmth and beauty.

The Baja Peninsula on the western side of Mexico separates the Gulf of California from the Pacific Ocean. It covers some 50,000 square miles with temperatures ranging from very hot in the dry deserts to icy in the mountains. Its very long shorelines draw many tourists and fishermen.

The Yucatan Peninsula juts out towards Cuba from Mexico and Guatemala and includes Belize. It covers about 75,000 square miles and separates the Gulf of Mexico from the Caribbean Sea. It has a hot, damp climate. Farmers grow many crops there, including corn, sugar cane, coffee, tobacco, and chicle – which is used in chewing gum.

Name _____

1 **This passage is —**

Ⓐ fiction.

Ⓑ from a social studies textbook.

Ⓒ an advertisement.

Ⓓ a play.

2 **The largest peninsula described here is —**

Ⓕ the Yucatan.

Ⓖ Baja California.

Ⓗ Mexico.

Ⓙ Florida.

3 **All peninsulas —**

Ⓐ are the same size.

Ⓑ are mostly surrounded by water.

Ⓒ produce oil.

Ⓓ are good for farming.

4 **Which peninsula is a state in the United States?**

Ⓕ Baja California

Ⓖ Florida

Ⓗ Yucatan

Ⓙ Atlantic

193

Name _____

Mark the mistakes in the following personal letter. Put ≡ under letters that should be capitals. Put ∧ to show where punctuation marks have been omitted. Can you find twenty (20) mistakes?

 1

219 south michigan street

chicago illinois 60603

may 14 2005

dear grandad

thank you for the rod and reel you sent me for my birthday last week when you come to

visit us this summer maybe we can go fishing at the lake i can use the boat if you are with

me

with love

Michael

Name _____

Fill in the bubble next to the word (article) that correctly completes each sentence.

1 Sedwick visited _____ castle in England.

Ⓐ a   Ⓑ an

2 They put _____ large new sign on the building.

Ⓕ a   Ⓖ an

3 The policeman handcuffed _____ unwilling suspect.

Ⓐ a   Ⓑ an

4 Kauai is _____ beautiful island in the state of Hawaii.

Ⓕ a   Ⓖ an

5 _____ old man was crossing the street.

Ⓐ A   Ⓑ An

6 The cruise took the tourists to _____ Alaskan glacier.

Ⓕ a   Ⓖ an

7 When you don't know what to do, call on _____ expert.

Ⓐ a   Ⓑ an

8 The committee needs _____ copy of the minutes for the March meeting.

Ⓕ a   Ⓖ an

195

Name _____

Read the outline and the student composition written from the outline. Answer the question.

Tornadoes
I.   What is a tornado?
II. Shape of a tornado
III. Where tornadoes occur
IV. Damage done by tornadoes

A tornado is a violent storm with strong twisting winds. From very dark clouds, a cone-shaped funnel seems to be coming down to earth. Tornadoes can occur anywhere in the world but mostly in the United States. Most last no more than an hour, traveling at sixty miles per hour or faster. Sometimes a funnel goes back into the clouds and then touches down again.

❶ Choose the sentence needed to complete the composition according to the outline.

Ⓐ Most tornadoes happen during warm or hot weather.

Ⓑ Tornadoes make a hissing or roaring sound.

Ⓒ A tornado can blow buildings apart and injure or kill people.

Ⓓ Tornadoes travel very fast.

Name _____

Using the dictionary's *guide words*, fill in the bubble next to the word that would be defined on that page.

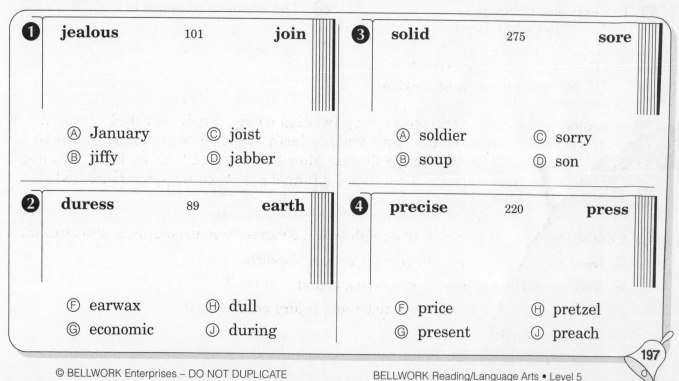

❶ jealous 101 **join**

- Ⓐ January
- Ⓑ jiffy
- Ⓒ joist
- Ⓓ jabber

❸ solid 275 **sore**

- Ⓐ soldier
- Ⓑ soup
- Ⓒ sorry
- Ⓓ son

❷ duress 89 **earth**

- Ⓕ earwax
- Ⓖ economic
- Ⓗ dull
- Ⓙ during

❹ precise 220 **press**

- Ⓕ price
- Ⓖ present
- Ⓗ pretzel
- Ⓙ preach

Name _____

Fill in the bubble next to the word (antonym) that correctly completes each sentence.

1 The *opposite* of <u>rough</u> is —

Ⓐ right.
Ⓑ smooth.
Ⓒ scratchy.
Ⓓ tough.

2 The *opposite* of <u>wide</u> is —

Ⓕ long.
Ⓖ big.
Ⓗ narrow.
Ⓙ wild.

3 The *opposite* of <u>smile</u> is —

Ⓐ laugh.
Ⓑ grin.
Ⓒ frown.
Ⓓ clown.

4 The *opposite* of <u>ill</u> is —

Ⓕ ail.
Ⓖ sick.
Ⓗ unwell.
Ⓙ healthy.

Name _____

Number each group of words in alphabetical order.

1

____ discover
____ desert
____ downstairs
____ downtown

2

____ count
____ country
____ county
____ countries

3

____ bowl
____ blanket
____ breakfast
____ breakdown

4

____ James Madison
____ James Monroe
____ George Washington
____ Abraham Lincoln

Name _____

Read each group of words. Then choose the word that does *not* belong.

❶
shirt	boots	sandals	shoes
Ⓐ	Ⓑ	Ⓒ	Ⓓ

❷
bedspread	blanket	rug	quilt
Ⓕ	Ⓖ	Ⓗ	Ⓙ

❸
minute	calendar	hour	second
Ⓐ	Ⓑ	Ⓒ	Ⓓ

❹
book	magazine	newspaper	notebook
Ⓕ	Ⓖ	Ⓗ	Ⓙ

Name _____

Read each set of sentences and decide if one of the <u>underlined words</u> is spelled *incorrectly*, or if there is *no mistake*. Choose your answer and fill in the bubble.

Ⓐ Tie those <u>paperes</u> up tightly with string.

Ⓑ The sun is too bright to <u>stare</u> at.

Ⓒ My brother is <u>thirteen</u> years old.

Ⓓ no mistake

Ⓕ She <u>omited</u> one word from that list.

Ⓖ The plum was ripe, but the peach was <u>sour</u>.

Ⓗ Last year our baseball team was <u>undefeated</u>.

Ⓙ no mistake

Ⓐ I <u>beleive</u> what you said is true.

Ⓑ The horses are in the <u>corral</u>.

Ⓒ Where would you like your <u>picture</u> hung?

Ⓓ no mistake

Ⓕ Our dog <u>choowed</u> the paper to shreds.

Ⓖ Please come join in our <u>discussion</u>.

Ⓗ Did you <u>receive</u> my gift today or yesterday?

Ⓙ no mistake

201

Name _____

After studying the map on this page, fill in the bubble next to the *best* answer.

1 **From the map you can tell that Florida is —**

Ⓐ an island.
Ⓑ a peninsula.
Ⓒ completely surrounded by water.
Ⓓ called the Sunshine State.

Florida, the Peninsula State

2 **Jacksonville is _____ of Miami.**

Ⓕ north   Ⓗ south
Ⓖ east   Ⓙ west

3 **Orlando is _____ of the state.**

Ⓐ in the upper part
Ⓑ in the lower part
Ⓒ toward the center
Ⓓ in the western part

4 **The Atlantic Ocean is on the _____ coast of Florida.**

Ⓕ north   Ⓗ south
Ⓖ east   Ⓙ west

Name _____

Fill in the bubble next to the answer that correctly completes each sentence.

1 The word <u>drove</u> is *closest in meaning to* —

Ⓐ move.

Ⓑ grove.

Ⓒ left.

Ⓓ drive.

2 The word <u>went</u> is *closest in meaning to* —

Ⓕ go.

Ⓖ done.

Ⓗ we.

Ⓙ wept.

3 The word <u>heard</u> is *closest in meaning to* —

Ⓐ here.

Ⓑ hear.

Ⓒ herd.

Ⓓ her.

4 The word <u>sang</u> is *closest in meaning to* —

Ⓕ tune.

Ⓖ play.

Ⓗ sing.

Ⓙ hum.

203

Name _____

Fill in the bubble next to the answer that is capitalized correctly.

1
ⓐ *Thomas And The Giant Apple Tree* was made into a movie.

ⓑ *Thomas and The Giant Apple Tree* was made into a movie.

ⓒ *Thomas and the Giant Apple Tree* was made into a movie.

2
ⓕ Jerrad said, "maybe we can go to the beach."

ⓖ Jerrad said, "Maybe we can go to the beach."

ⓗ Jerrad said, "maybe we can go to the Beach."

3
ⓐ Frank Blum is the author of *the lost Treasure*.

ⓑ Frank Blum is the author of *The Lost treasure*.

ⓒ Frank Blum is the author of *The Lost Treasure*.

4
ⓕ T. R. Randall, author of *Martha's Maze*, also wrote *The legend of the Swan*.

ⓖ T. R. Randall, author of *Martha's Maze*, also wrote *The Legend of the Swan*.

ⓗ T. R. Randall, author of *Martha's Maze*, also wrote *The Legend of The Swan*.

Page _____

A

1. Ⓐ Ⓑ Ⓒ Ⓓ Ⓔ
2. Ⓕ Ⓖ Ⓗ Ⓙ Ⓚ
3. Ⓐ Ⓑ Ⓒ Ⓓ Ⓔ
4. Ⓕ Ⓖ Ⓗ Ⓙ Ⓚ

Page _____

B

1. Ⓐ Ⓑ Ⓒ Ⓓ Ⓔ
2. Ⓕ Ⓖ Ⓗ Ⓙ Ⓚ
3. Ⓐ Ⓑ Ⓒ Ⓓ Ⓔ
4. Ⓕ Ⓖ Ⓗ Ⓙ Ⓚ

Page _____

C

1. Ⓐ Ⓑ Ⓒ Ⓓ Ⓔ
2. Ⓕ Ⓖ Ⓗ Ⓙ Ⓚ
3. Ⓐ Ⓑ Ⓒ Ⓓ Ⓔ
4. Ⓕ Ⓖ Ⓗ Ⓙ Ⓚ

Page _____

D

1. Ⓐ Ⓑ Ⓒ Ⓓ Ⓔ
2. Ⓕ Ⓖ Ⓗ Ⓙ Ⓚ
3. Ⓐ Ⓑ Ⓒ Ⓓ Ⓔ
4. Ⓕ Ⓖ Ⓗ Ⓙ Ⓚ

Page _____

E

1. Ⓐ Ⓑ Ⓒ Ⓓ Ⓔ
2. Ⓕ Ⓖ Ⓗ Ⓙ Ⓚ
3. Ⓐ Ⓑ Ⓒ Ⓓ Ⓔ
4. Ⓕ Ⓖ Ⓗ Ⓙ Ⓚ

Page _____

F

1. Ⓐ Ⓑ Ⓒ Ⓓ Ⓔ
2. Ⓕ Ⓖ Ⓗ Ⓙ Ⓚ
3. Ⓐ Ⓑ Ⓒ Ⓓ Ⓔ
4. Ⓕ Ⓖ Ⓗ Ⓙ Ⓚ

Page _____

G

1. Ⓐ Ⓑ Ⓒ Ⓓ Ⓔ
2. Ⓕ Ⓖ Ⓗ Ⓙ Ⓚ
3. Ⓐ Ⓑ Ⓒ Ⓓ Ⓔ
4. Ⓕ Ⓖ Ⓗ Ⓙ Ⓚ

Page _____

H

1. Ⓐ Ⓑ Ⓒ Ⓓ Ⓔ
2. Ⓕ Ⓖ Ⓗ Ⓙ Ⓚ
3. Ⓐ Ⓑ Ⓒ Ⓓ Ⓔ
4. Ⓕ Ⓖ Ⓗ Ⓙ Ⓚ

Page _____

I

1. Ⓐ Ⓑ Ⓒ Ⓓ Ⓔ
2. Ⓕ Ⓖ Ⓗ Ⓙ Ⓚ
3. Ⓐ Ⓑ Ⓒ Ⓓ Ⓔ
4. Ⓕ Ⓖ Ⓗ Ⓙ Ⓚ

Page _____

J

1. Ⓐ Ⓑ Ⓒ Ⓓ Ⓔ
2. Ⓕ Ⓖ Ⓗ Ⓙ Ⓚ
3. Ⓐ Ⓑ Ⓒ Ⓓ Ⓔ
4. Ⓕ Ⓖ Ⓗ Ⓙ Ⓚ

Page _____

K

1. Ⓐ Ⓑ Ⓒ Ⓓ Ⓔ
2. Ⓕ Ⓖ Ⓗ Ⓙ Ⓚ
3. Ⓐ Ⓑ Ⓒ Ⓓ Ⓔ
4. Ⓕ Ⓖ Ⓗ Ⓙ Ⓚ

Page _____

L

1. Ⓐ Ⓑ Ⓒ Ⓓ Ⓔ
2. Ⓕ Ⓖ Ⓗ Ⓙ Ⓚ
3. Ⓐ Ⓑ Ⓒ Ⓓ Ⓔ
4. Ⓕ Ⓖ Ⓗ Ⓙ Ⓚ

Page _____

A

1. Ⓐ Ⓑ Ⓒ Ⓓ Ⓔ
2. Ⓕ Ⓖ Ⓗ Ⓙ Ⓚ
3. Ⓐ Ⓑ Ⓒ Ⓓ Ⓔ
4. Ⓕ Ⓖ Ⓗ Ⓙ Ⓚ

Page _____

B

1. Ⓐ Ⓑ Ⓒ Ⓓ Ⓔ
2. Ⓕ Ⓖ Ⓗ Ⓙ Ⓚ
3. Ⓐ Ⓑ Ⓒ Ⓓ Ⓔ
4. Ⓕ Ⓖ Ⓗ Ⓙ Ⓚ

Page _____

C

1. Ⓐ Ⓑ Ⓒ Ⓓ Ⓔ
2. Ⓕ Ⓖ Ⓗ Ⓙ Ⓚ
3. Ⓐ Ⓑ Ⓒ Ⓓ Ⓔ
4. Ⓕ Ⓖ Ⓗ Ⓙ Ⓚ

Page _____

D

1. Ⓐ Ⓑ Ⓒ Ⓓ Ⓔ
2. Ⓕ Ⓖ Ⓗ Ⓙ Ⓚ
3. Ⓐ Ⓑ Ⓒ Ⓓ Ⓔ
4. Ⓕ Ⓖ Ⓗ Ⓙ Ⓚ

Page _____

E

1. Ⓐ Ⓑ Ⓒ Ⓓ Ⓔ
2. Ⓕ Ⓖ Ⓗ Ⓙ Ⓚ
3. Ⓐ Ⓑ Ⓒ Ⓓ Ⓔ
4. Ⓕ Ⓖ Ⓗ Ⓙ Ⓚ

Page _____

F

1. Ⓐ Ⓑ Ⓒ Ⓓ Ⓔ
2. Ⓕ Ⓖ Ⓗ Ⓙ Ⓚ
3. Ⓐ Ⓑ Ⓒ Ⓓ Ⓔ
4. Ⓕ Ⓖ Ⓗ Ⓙ Ⓚ

Page _____

G

1. Ⓐ Ⓑ Ⓒ Ⓓ Ⓔ
2. Ⓕ Ⓖ Ⓗ Ⓙ Ⓚ
3. Ⓐ Ⓑ Ⓒ Ⓓ Ⓔ
4. Ⓕ Ⓖ Ⓗ Ⓙ Ⓚ

Page _____

H

1. Ⓐ Ⓑ Ⓒ Ⓓ Ⓔ
2. Ⓕ Ⓖ Ⓗ Ⓙ Ⓚ
3. Ⓐ Ⓑ Ⓒ Ⓓ Ⓔ
4. Ⓕ Ⓖ Ⓗ Ⓙ Ⓚ

Page _____

I

1. Ⓐ Ⓑ Ⓒ Ⓓ Ⓔ
2. Ⓕ Ⓖ Ⓗ Ⓙ Ⓚ
3. Ⓐ Ⓑ Ⓒ Ⓓ Ⓔ
4. Ⓕ Ⓖ Ⓗ Ⓙ Ⓚ

Page _____

J

1. Ⓐ Ⓑ Ⓒ Ⓓ Ⓔ
2. Ⓕ Ⓖ Ⓗ Ⓙ Ⓚ
3. Ⓐ Ⓑ Ⓒ Ⓓ Ⓔ
4. Ⓕ Ⓖ Ⓗ Ⓙ Ⓚ

Page _____

K

1. Ⓐ Ⓑ Ⓒ Ⓓ Ⓔ
2. Ⓕ Ⓖ Ⓗ Ⓙ Ⓚ
3. Ⓐ Ⓑ Ⓒ Ⓓ Ⓔ
4. Ⓕ Ⓖ Ⓗ Ⓙ Ⓚ

Page _____

L

1. Ⓐ Ⓑ Ⓒ Ⓓ Ⓔ
2. Ⓕ Ⓖ Ⓗ Ⓙ Ⓚ
3. Ⓐ Ⓑ Ⓒ Ⓓ Ⓔ
4. Ⓕ Ⓖ Ⓗ Ⓙ Ⓚ